Science Works

3

Philippa Gardom-Hulme

Pam Large

Sandra Mitchell

Chris Sherry

OXFORD

UNIVERSITY PRESS

OXFORD
UNIVERSITY PRESS

Great Clarendon Street, Oxford OX2 6DP

Oxford University Press is a department of the University of Oxford.
It furthers the University's objective of excellence in research, scholarship,
and education by publishing worldwide in

Oxford   New York

Auckland   Cape Town   Dar es Salaam   Hong Kong   Karachi
Kuala Lumpur   Madrid   Melbourne   Mexico City   Nairobi
New Delhi   Shanghai   Taipei   Toronto

With offices in

Argentina   Austria   Brazil   Chile   Czech Republic   France   Greece
Guatemala   Hungary   Italy   Japan   Poland   Portugal   Singapore
South Korea   Switzerland   Thailand   Turkey   Ukraine   Vietnam

© Oxford University Press

The moral rights of the authors have been asserted

Database right Oxford University Press (maker)

First published 2009

British Library Cataloguing in Publication Data

Data available

ISBN: 978-0-19-915254-4

10 9 8 7 6 5 4 3 2

Printed in China by Printplus

Paper used in the production of this book is a natural, recyclable product made
from wood grown in sustainable forests. The manufacturing process conforms to
the environmental regulations to the country of origin.

Acknowledgements

The publisher and authors would like to thank the following for permission to use
photographs and other copyright material:

Cover image: Westend61 GmbH/Alamy.

P6t Damir Cudic/iStockphoto; P6bl Daniel Berehulak/Getty Images; P6br
Juanmonino/iStockphoto; P7t John Bavosi/Science Photo Library; P7m Centers
for disease Control and Prevention; P7b David H. Wells/Corbis; P9 Edelmann/
Science Photo Library; P12ml Piotr Enge/iStockphoto; P12t iStockphoto; P12mr Enge/
iStockphoto; P14 Michael Blackburn/iStockphoto; P15 James Nachtwey/VII; P16t
Andy Crump, Tdr, Who/Science Photo Library; P16m Scott Bauer/Us Department Of
Agriculture/Science Photo Library; P17 Lucian/iStockphoto; P18tl Richard Hobson
Photography/iStockphoto; P18tr Catherine Ursillo/Science Photo Library; P18m
Scott Camazine/Science Photo Library; P18b Medical Rf.Com/Science Photo Library;
P19t Sam Ogden/Science Photo Library; P19m Vanessa Vick/Science Photo Library;
P20t Jung Yeon-Je/AFP; P20b Peter Menzel/Science Photo Library; P21l Yuriko Nakao/
Reuters; P21r OUP Picture Bank; P22t Georgijevic Miroslav/Shutterstock; P22b
Mikkel William Nielsen/iStockphoto; P23tl Antonia Reeve/Science Photo Library;
P23tr Lisa F. Young/iStockphoto; P23m Antonia Reeve/Science Photo Library;
P23mb Lisa F. Young/iStockphoto; P23b Timothy Babasade/iStockphoto; P24t Mike
Finn-Kelcey/Reuters; P24b Friedrich Saurer/Science Photo Library; P26 Mills, Andy/
Star Ledger/Corbis; P27 Medimage/Science Photo Library; P28t Simone van den
Berg/iStockphoto; P28b technotr/iStockphoto; P29t Robert Ghement/EPA; P29ml
Yuri Arcurs/iStockphoto; P29mr Mike Hewitt/Getty Images; P30t Samuel Ashfield/
Science Photo Library; P30m Anatomical Travelogue/Science Photo Library; P31t
Richard List/Corbis; P31m Juergen Berger/Science Photo Library; P31b Simon
Fraser/RVI, Newcastle-Upon-Tyne/Science Photo Library; P32t NASA; P32m NASA;
P32b NASA; P33t NASA; P33b NASA; P34t Alexander Tsiaras/Science Photo Library;
P34m Life In View/Science Photo Library; P35t Sam Ogden/Science Photo Library;
P35m Images courtesy of the Hospital Clínic of Barcelona(http://blog.hospitalclinic.
org) University of Bristol (UK), University of Padua (Italy) and University of Milan
(Italy); P36t Life In View/Science Photo Library; P36b John Bavosi/Science Photo
Library; P38t Jeyakumar Ramanji/iStockphoto; P38m Wayne Lawler/Science
Photo Library; P38b OUP Picture Bank; P39 Ray Roper/iStockphoto; P40t Dieter
Spears/iStockphoto; P40m Per Christiansen/Zoological Museum Copenhagen; P41
David Lambert/iStockphoto; P42t moodboard/Corbis; P42b Anthony Mercieca/
Science Photo Library; P43t Mountain Pine Beetle (Dendroctonus ponderosae), ©
Department of Natural Resources Canada, 1998. All rights reserved.; P43b Serdar
Uckun/iStockphoto; P44t Edward Shaw/iStockphoto; P44b Sinclair Stammers/

Science Photo Library; P45t Mayumi Terao/iStockphoto; P45m Pascal Goetgheluck/
Science Photo Library; P45b Vaughan Fleming/Science Photo Library; P46t Geoff
Tompkinson/Science Photo Library; P46b Zeynep Mufti/iStockphoto; P48t Piotr
Skubisz/Dreamstime; P48m Philippe Psaila/Science Photo Library; P48b Graeme
Purdy/iStockphoto; P49t WTPL/Victor de Jesus; P49m Ron Hilton/iStockphoto; P49b
Philip Lee Harvey/Getty; P50 Ria Novosti/Science Photo Library; P51ml Torsten
Lorenz/Dreamstime; P51mr Forest & Kim Starr; P52m Ho New/Reuters; P52b Gary
Hincks/Science Photo Library; P53m Sheila Terry/Science Photo Library; P53b Ted
Kinsman/Science Photo Library; P54t Dragan Trifunovic/iStockphoto; P54m Science
Photo Library; P55l Zeka/iStockphoto; P55r Prill Mediendesign & Fotografie/
iStockphoto; P56 Jurie Maree/iStockphoto; P57t Lepus/Science Photo Library;
P57m British Antarctic Survey/Science Photo Library; P58 Keith Hiscock; P59
Gerry/iStockphoto; P60t Gregory Dimijian/Science Photo Library; P60m Andrew J.
Martinez/Science Photo Library; P61t Dirk Wiersma/Science Photo Library; P61m
Dheera Venkatraman; P62t Maxine Adcock/Science Photo Library; P62b Paulo
Cruz/iStockphoto; P64t OUP Picture Bank; P64m Nasa/Science Photo Library; P64b
Eva Serrabassa/iStockphoto; P65 Julia Milberger/iStockphoto; P66t Joze Pojbic/
iStockphoto; P66b Forrest M. Mims III; P67 Weforum/Remy Steinegger; 68tl
Ronen/iStockphoto; P68m Olivier Blondeau/iStockphoto; P68tr Wolfgang Amri/
iStockphoto; P68b Gordon Dixon/iStockphoto; P69 C J Sherry; P70t Joe Raedle/
Getty Images; P70m Eye Of Science/Science Photo Library; P70b Nancy Louie/
iStockphoto; P72t © Bloodhound Programme Ltd 2009 All Rights Reserved; P72b
Ken Goff/Contributor/WireImage/Getty Images; P73t Kevin Parry/Contributor/
WireImage/Getty Images; P73bl BMW Group; P73br BMW Group; P74 Sean Gallup/
Getty Images; P75t David McNew/Getty Images; P75b David McNew/Getty Images;
P76l Richard Vogel; P76r www.channel4.com/4car; P77 Ivan Cholakov/iStockphoto;
P78t OUP Picture Bank; P78m OUP Picture Bank; P80t Lars Lindblad/iStockphoto;
P80b Navcon Engineering Network – SoundPLAN; P81 Casella Measurement
Limited; P82t Silent Aircraft Initiative; P82b Kris Hanke/iStockphoto; P83 Silent
Aircraft Initiative; P84m Peter Ryan/Science Photo Library; P84b Howard Davies/
Corbis; P85t Marcelo Wain/iStockphoto; P85m International Rivers; P86t Image
Source/Corbis; P86m Phil Augustavo/iStockphoto; P86b C J Sherry; P87 Martyn F.
Chillmaid/Science Photo Library; P88m Edward Rokita;

P88b Ann Taylor-Hughes/iStockphoto; P90t Andrea Skjold/iStockphoto;

P90m Alexander Raths/Shutterstock; P91m BorisKhamitsevich/iStockphoto; P91b
Jonathan Heger/Shutterstock;

P92t Liz Hafalia/San Francisco Chronicle/Corbis; P92m Ecosphere Technologies;
P93tl Environment Agency, Thames Region and South West Water; P93tm Lachlan
Currie/iStockphoto; P93tr Chris Crafter/iStockphoto; P95t Fred Fox/iStockphoto;
P95m Ian Norris;

P96t Arthur Kwiatkowski/iStockphoto; P96m C J Sherry; P96b Geoffrey Hammond/
iStockphoto; P97t Mike Bentley/iStockphoto; P97b Wibofoto/iStockphoto; P98t
George Green/iStockphoto; P98m Lawrence Karn/iStockphoto; P99 NASA Jet
Propulsion Laboratory (NASA-JPL); P100t NASA Marshall Space Flight Center
(NASA-MSFC); P100m NASA; P100b OUP Picture Bank; P101t Wallace & Gromit: A
Grand Day Out © NFTS 1989; P101m Carol Gering/iStockphoto; P102 Mark Ralston/
AFP; P103t Darryn Lyons/Daily Mail/Rex Features; P103m Jeffrey A. Hoffman/
NASA; P104t NASA; P104m NASA; P104b STScI/Hubblesite/NASA; P105t NASA, ESA
and Paul Kalas/UC Berkeley; P105m STScI/NASA/Hubblesite; P106t Ria Novosti/
Science Photo Library; P106m NASA; P106b JSC/NASA; P107l NASA; P107r NASA/
Science Photo Library; P108t NASA; P108b NASA; P110t NASA; P110b NASA; P111m
Courtesy NASA/JPL-Caltech; P111b Mark Parisi/offthemark.com; P112t NASA/JPL/
University of Arizona; P112m NASA; P112mb NASA/Science Photo Library; P112b
NASA/Science Photo Library; P113 Corby Waste/JPL/NASA; P114t C J Sherry; P114b
Lynmouth & Lynton Lift Co.; P115 Tony Steenmeyer (Cliff Railways of the British
Isles Oakwood Press 2002); P116t OUP Picture Bank; P116m iStockphoto; P116b
David Nunuk/Science Photo Library; P117t Cordelia Molloy/Science Photo Library;
P117m George Clerk/iStockphoto; P118tl Michelle Van Meter/iStockphoto; P118tr
iStockphoto; P118b John Booth; P121t Carmen Martínez Banus/iStockphoto;
P121b Terraxplorer/iStockphoto; P122 Kativ/iStockphoto; P123 Hans F Meier/
iStockphoto P124m Covalent Solar; P124m Manan Vatsyayana/AFP; P124b Mark
A. Philbrick/Brigham Young University; P125t Issei Kato/Reuters; P125m Gene
Chutka/iStockphoto; P126 Drax Power Limited; P127t OnFilm/iStockphoto; P127m Alvin Smith inventor of SEARASER; P128t meldayus/iStockphoto; P128m
Andrew Aitchison/Ashden Awards; P128b Andrew Aitchison/Ashden Awards;
P129m Timothy Large/iStckphoto; P129b Ralph/iStockphoto; P130t Stephen Hird/
Reuters/Corbis; P130b Scase News Service Ltd; P131 Reix - Liewig/For Picture/
Corbis; P132 XAVIER BERTRAL/epa/Corbis; P134t AFP/Getty Images; P134m
MistikaS/iStockphoto; P134b Mike King/Corbis; P135t Gilbert Iundt/TempSport/
Corbis; P135b technotr/iStockphoto; P136t P_Wei/iStockphoto; P136ml TommL/
iStockphoto; P136mr TommL/iStockphoto; P136b Artur Achtelik/iStockphoto;
P138t Tim de Waele/Corbis; P138m Lotus Engineering; P139tl Andy Sacks/Getty
Images; P139tr Jerry Cooke/Corbis; P140t AFP/Getty Images; P140m Jon Patton/
iStockphoto; P140m Bob Thomas Sports Photography/Getty Images; P140b Alex
Nikada/iStockphoto; P142l William Loy/iStockphoto; P142r Jamie Squire/Getty
Images; P143t Sports Illustrated/Getty Images; P143b Sports Illustrated/Getty
Images; P144 Schlegelmilch/Corbis; P145 Bruce Benedict/TRANSTOCK/Transtock/
Corbis.

Technical illustrations are by Steve Evans and other illustrations by Rui Ricardo.

This book is called *Science Works* because it shows you how scientists work out their ideas about the world, *and* how science can be put to work in everyday life.

It will help you:

- Develop your understanding of scientific ideas
- Work out scientific ideas for yourself using results from investigations
- See how science is used in everyday life
- Think about how we can use science for the best

The book has two types of pages. Most are like this:

'Learn about' lists your objectives for the topic

'Green' sections introduce the topic simply

'Red' headings are to make you think much harder!

'Amber' sections move on to more detail and slightly harder ideas

'Get this' boxes tell what you should know from the topic

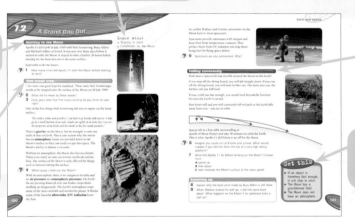

In every unit there are also some pages called 'How Science Works' which looks at science in action. This might be how scientists develop theories and find evidence, how to find patterns in data, how science is used in jobs or how science affects our lives.

All the key words you need to know are in **bold** and they are all defined in a glossary at the book. You'll also find an index right at the back to help you find the information you want.

We hope *Science Works* will help you think about science, understand it and, above all, enjoy it!

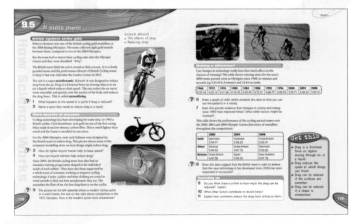

Contents

shows which are the special 'How Science Works' pages (but you'll find out about how science works on other pages too).

Biology

Chemistry

Physics

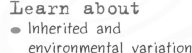
Family

Natalia and Kuba have something to celebrate. Kasia – their first child – was born today.

Kasia has **inherited** some of each parent's **features**. Some are already obvious, like her skin colour and blood group. Others, like the sound of her voice and her final height, won't develop until she is older.

The features Kasia inherited from her parents are controlled by **genes**. She got half her genes from her mother and half from her father. The set from each parent was a random selection so her parents couldn't predict which features she would inherit. The variety caused by genes mixing when babies are conceived is **inherited variation.**

Kasia's genes determined many of her features before she was born, and they will affect her for the rest of her life.

1 What decides the features you inherit?

2 Kuba thinks Kasia will inherit his creativity and be brilliant at maths like Natalia. Explain why this might not happen?

Other influences

Genes are not the only things which shape us. We are also affected by our surroundings and the things that happen to us.

Children who don't get enough to eat can't grow to their full height, and suffer health problems. Those who eat too much are fatter than they should be and more likely to suffer from heart disease or diabetes later. Diseases and drug use also affect our bodies. Variety that develops in these ways is called **environmental variation**.

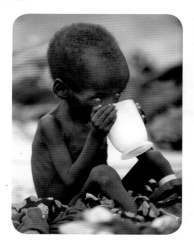 

By the time Kasia was born, her features had been influenced by the environment in Natalia's uterus.

3 Use an example to explain how your environment can affect your features?

4 Kuba thinks the features Kasia has already are caused by her genes and the ones that will develop later are caused by her environment. Is he right?

Your first environment

When she was growing in Natalia's womb, Kasia needed nutrients and a steady supply of oxygen. She took them from Natalia's blood using her **umbilical cord** and **placenta**.

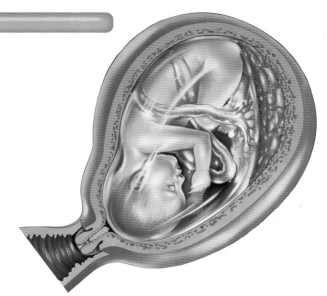

 5 How do developing embryos get nutrients to build new **cells** and maintain their energy supply?

Protected?

A fetus looks safe inside her mother's **uterus** but it is very vulnerable. Drugs and infections can cross the placenta and do damage, especially during the first 12 weeks when its organs are developing.

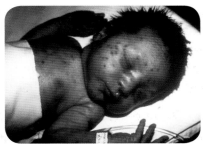

Jordan is deaf and blind. Her brain didn't grow properly and many of her other organs are damaged. Her mum caught rubella before she realised she was pregnant. These days most women have had the MMR (mumps, measles and rubella) vaccination. This makes them immune to the virus, so their babies are protected too.

 6 When is a fetus most vulnerable to drugs and infections?

Kevin has a poor memory and he finds it difficult to concentrate in lessons. The distinctive shape of his face shows he is suffering from fetal alcohol syndrome. His mother drank a lot before she realised she was pregnant.

Doctors used to think it took a lot of alcohol to harm a baby. Now they know that even small amounts make a lasting difference.

 7 Why are pregnant women advised not to drink at all?

Summing up

8 Pregnant women are checked to see if they are immune to rubella. What could happen if they are not?

9 What two things determine your features?

10 Women who are trying to start a family are advised to eat healthily and stop smoking and drinking. Explain why.

Get this

- Our features are influenced by the genes we inherit.
- They are also influenced by environmental factors like our intake of nutrients.

1.2 New life

Learn about
- How genes control development

Passing on genes

Most of Natalia and Kuba's cells have two copies of every gene, but their **sex cells** only have one of each.

When the genes in Kuba's sperm entered Natalia's egg, their **embryo** got a new, combination of genes. It used the recipes in these genes to construct Kasia's body, so she will be different from everyone else.

1 Explain how an embryo ends up with a full set of genes.

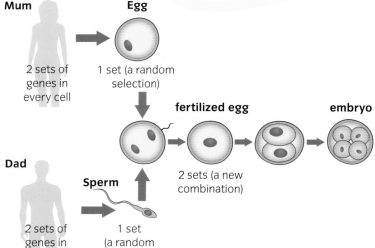

Mum — 2 sets of genes in every cell

Egg — 1 set (a random selection)

Dad — 2 sets of genes in every cell

Sperm — 1 set (a random selection)

fertilized egg — 2 sets (a new combination)

embryo

Making copies

How did the genes from the **fertilised** egg get into all Kasia's **cells**?

The egg divided into two, then both cells divided to make four, and so on.

Before it divided, each of Kasia's cells copied its nucleus, with all its genes. So all her new cells got an identical set of genes.

2 How do genes from your parents get into every cell in your body?

To begin with Kasia's cells were **stem cells**. They could produce any other type of cell.

As they carried on dividing, her cells became more **specialised**. Some formed a placenta and implanted themselves in Natalia's uterus. Others formed Kasia's embryonic body. They became muscle cells, nerve cells, parts of her eyes, etc.

She has 200 different cell types now, but they all have identical genes.

3 What are stem cells?

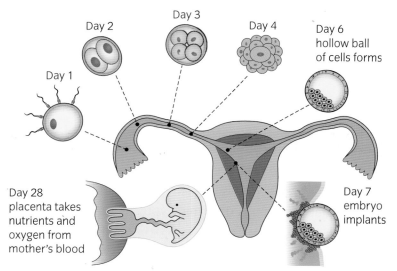

Day 1

Day 2

Day 3

Day 4

Day 6 hollow ball of cells forms

Day 7 embryo implants

Day 28 placenta takes nutrients and oxygen from mother's blood

Becoming human

Kasia's embryo has been growing for ten weeks. She is floating freely in her amniotic sac. The fluid around her protects her from jolts and gives her space to move.

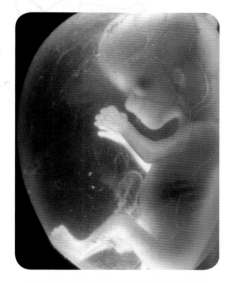

Her cells have specialised completely, arranged themselves into **tissues** and **organs**, and taken on different roles.

Kasia is practising things she'll do when she is born. Her brain uses nerve cells to make her muscle cells contract. She waves her arms and legs, sucks her thumb and breathes the amniotic fluid in and out. Sensors in her skin send signals to her developing brain. Her other senses will join in as soon as they are formed.

4 How do balls of identical cells turn into babies?

5 What jobs do nerves and muscles do?

6 Which sense organs develop first?

Passing on instructions

Kasia has inherited many of Natalia and Kuba's features. Some features are always passed on if their parents have them. With others it's a matter of chance.

Emma is tall but her parents are very short. Her older brother is short too. **Environmental factors** – like not having the right nutrients – can limit growth, but her parents and brother have always had good diets.

Both Emma's parents have an unusual gene. It stops them reaching their expected maximum height. The effect is called achondroplasia. Her brother inherited this feature, but why hasn't Emma?

7 Is the height difference between Emma and her parents caused by genetic or environmental factors?

Summing up

8 What does fertilisation involve?

9 Why is Kasia different from anybody else?

10 What happened to Kasia's cells as they increased in number?

11 When Natalia was 20 weeks pregnant she started to feel Kasia moving around inside her. Why does a fetus move around?

Get this

- A new life forms when a sperm fertilises an egg.
- Every embryo has a unique combination of genes.
- Genes make embryonic cells specialise and organise themselves into tissues and organs.

Learn about
● Mendel's experiments

Learning from plants

Creative thinking by a monk called Gregor Mendel began to explain **inheritance** 150 years ago –before genes were discovered.

Mendel worked with tall and short pea plants. Each pea flower makes male and female sex cells, so they can self-pollinate and produce identical tall or short offspring.

Mendel stopped flowers self-pollinating by taking away their pollen. Then he used a brush to make pollen from one sort of pea plant fertilise the other.

All their offspring were tall.

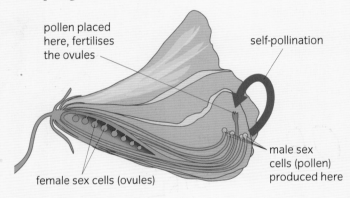

pollen placed here, fertilises the ovules

self-pollination

male sex cells (pollen) produced here

female sex cells (ovules)

When these tall plants fertilised each other, some of the third generation were short.

? **1**   Did Mendel's second generation pea plants inherit their parents' features?

2   How did Mendel make sure that the tall and short plants could only fertilise each other?

Mendel's theory

Mendel's **theory** was that two 'factors' control each feature – one from each parent. These 'factors' are now called genes.

The genes in a pair can be the same or different. One gene makes peas tall; another makes them short. When peas have one of each, they are always tall.

Genes that stop other versions having an effect are called **dominant** genes.

? **3**   The gene that makes peas tall is a dominant gene. How can you tell?

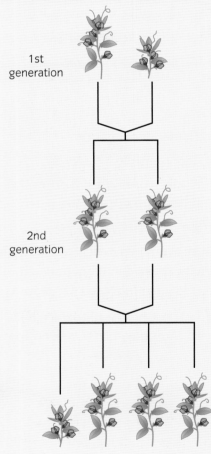

1st generation

2nd generation

3rd generation

So where did the short plants come from in the third generation?

Mendel invented a code to explain what happens. In the diagram on the opposite page 'T' shows the dominant gene and 't' shows the version that makes plants short.

In the first generation, the tall plants have two T genes, so all their sex cells (pollen and ovules) have one. The short plants have two t versions, so all their sex cells have a t gene.

The second generation plants inherit a gene from each parent so they have both sorts: T and t. The T version is dominant so the pea plants are all tall.

 4 Why are the second generation plants all tall?

Each of the second generation plants makes two sorts of sex cells. On average, half carry T and half carry t, so many of the offspring will have Tt again. But male sex cells carrying 'T' or 't' could fertilise female sex cells with the same gene. So plants with TT or tt genes could also be made.

The TT and Tt plants are tall. But the tt plants are short because they don't have the dominant T gene.

 5 Explain why some of the third generation plants are short.

6 How would the 2nd and 3rd generation plants be different if shortness dominated tallness?

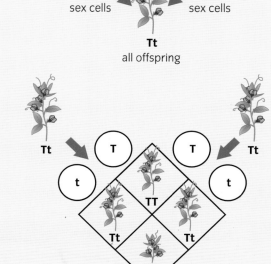

Emma's genes

Emma's parents both have an unusual gene which limits bone growth. It stops people reaching their expected maximum height. Both of them also have a normal gene for bone growth but the faulty gene is the dominant one so it controls their height.

Emma happened to inherit two copies of the normal version of the gene. This means that nothing limits her growth.

Summing up

7 What is a dominant gene?

8 Draw a diagram to show why Emma didn't inherit the faulty gene. Use A to represent the dominant faulty gene.

9 Tony has red hair but both his parents have brown hair. Explain how this could have happened.

Get this

- Our features are influenced by the genes we inherit.
- Genes come in pairs.
- When one gene in a pair is dominant it controls that feature.

Evidence from twins

Doubles

Kate and Rachel are **identical twins**. They were formed from one egg and one sperm and started out as one embryo. When the embryo was a few days old, it split into two groups of cells and each of these formed one baby. So they both have identical sets of genes.

The twins are the same sex, and look very like each other. But they have distinct personalities, like different music and choose different clothes.

Can genes make you artistic, sporty or good at telling jokes? Or do skills like these depend on environmental factors like how your parents bring you up, the school you go to and the friends you hang around with?

 1 Are identical twins totally identical?

Bad science?

In 1970 a New York adoption agency let different families adopt identical twin babies without saying they were twins. **Psychologists** visited each home to see if their environments could make them grow more different than twins raised together. The results were never published.

Thirty three years later one pair met. They look alike, have the same allergies and chose the same careers, but they have different pets. One is a vegetarian, one a smoker and one has had a happier life.

2 What was good about the design of the experiment?

3 Suggest why experiments like this are no longer allowed.

What do genes influence?

To get reliable **evidence** about genetic and environmental influences, you need to study thousands of twins. Scientists often compare identical and **non-identical** pairs.

Non-identical twins form when two different eggs are fertilised at the same time. Like ordinary brothers and sisters they inherit different selections of their parents' genes. But they are the same age, like identical twins, and share the same environment. The only difference is that the non-identical twins share half as many genes.

In one study scientists compared the results identical and non-identical twins got in memory and verbal reasoning tests and their school exams. They looked at how close the results were for the twins in each pair.

The bar chart shows how close the results were across all the identical pairs and all the non-identical pairs. In the chart, 0 would mean no similarity between the pairs of twins in a group, and 1 would mean that their results were identical. The higher the bar, the more similar the twins' results.

If genes had no effect, the bars would be the same for each type of twin. The bigger the difference between the two types of twin, the more that feature is influenced by genes. Comparisons like this suggest that genes influence most of our features.

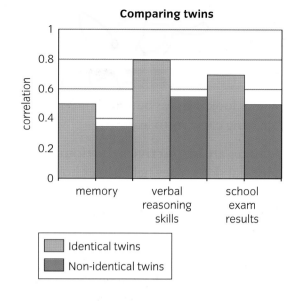

Comparing twins

 4 Which of the features in the chart seems to be most influenced by genes?

Destiny

Do genes decide your destiny, or does it depend on your environment?

Some animals have a gene that makes their brain cells produce less of a certain enzyme. Rats with this gene are more aggressive than others.

Psychologists studied people with the same gene to see if it always has the same effect. They compared the level of antisocial behaviour among people with and without the gene who grew up in different environments – some who had happy childhoods (no maltreatment) and some who had been very badly treated in childhood (severe maltreatment).

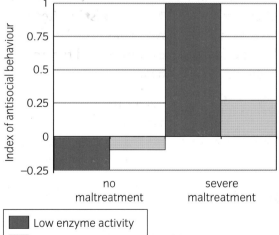

How maltreatment affects children with different genes

 5 What do the results show?

6 Do genes decide your exact features?

Summing up

7 Why are identical twins so useful to scientists?

8 What does twin data tell us about our features?

9 A newspaper headline reads: 'Bad behaviour gene found in 50% of boys'. Use what you know about genes to explain whether or not the statement could be true?

Get this

- Most of our features depend on both our genes and the way our environment affects us.

Changing behaviour

Learn about
- Instincts and learned behaviours

Helpless?

Babies look helpless but they inherit a host of useful **reflexes** and an amazing capacity to learn.

Reflexes are **instinctive behaviour patterns**. Some are physical skills. They help babies hold on to their mother, find a nipple, suck and swallow milk.

Other instincts are **social** skills that get them extra attention. They make eye contact, smile, respond to speech sounds and mimic their carer's expressions.

Instincts are predictable. The same **stimulus** causes the same effect in every baby. They fade away gradually as infants develop more flexible **learned behaviours**.

1 What is a stimulus?
2 Why are a baby's reflexes useful?
3 Which reflexes help a baby find food?
4 Which reflex is a surprising one for a newborn to have?

Reflex	Stimulus	Action
Startle	Loud noise or fast movement	Flings arms out
Rooting	Touch on cheek	Turns and opens mouth
Sucking	Something in mouth	Sucks
Grip	Touch on palm	Very strong grip
Swimming	Being under water	Holds breath and swims

Learning

Carl's mum cancels his pocket money if his bedroom is a mess, so he keeps it tidy. We all learn to do things that bring rewards and avoid negative consequences. But we are social animals, so we learn by **imitation** too.

In one experiment, young children saw a man hit a large doll. His behaviour was praised, punished or ignored. Then the children were left alone with the doll to see how many copied the behaviour.

5 Did more children imitate the adult's behaviour when it was rewarded?
6 Did seeing the behaviour punished stop them copying it?
7 How did the boys' behaviour differ from the girls'?

Learning by imitation

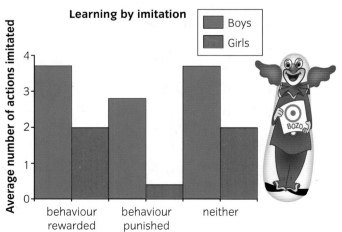

Average number of actions imitated

Boys
Girls

behaviour rewarded   behaviour punished   neither

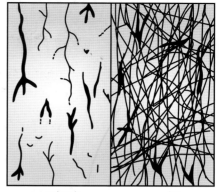

nerve cells in the brain

at birth   aged 7

A good start

When you were a baby your relatives gave you lots of attention. They cuddled you, talked to you and gave you interesting toys.

All that **stimulation** was good for your brain. Messages from your **sense organs** helped its nerve cells to link together. That made it easier for you to learn, and helped you to grow up happy and well behaved.

 8 What happens in a baby's brain as they listen and look around?

9 Parents are advised to sing to their babies and teach them nursery rhymes. Why is that good advice?

Scarred for life

In the 1990s thousands of babies were abandoned in Romanian orphanages without enough staff to look after them. Babies lay in cots all day and received very little stimulation.

	Months spent in Romanian orphanage		
	0	4	8+
Intelligence score	108	99	85
Language score	106	99	98
Behaviour problems	13%	9%	43%

When reporters uncovered the problem, many of the babies were adopted and taken abroad. Ten years later, Canadian psychologists compared these orphans with other adopted children. The table shows their results.

 10 What did this tragedy allow psychologists to study?

11 Which children were most affected by their early experiences?

12 What were the main problems the children suffered from?

Summing up

13 How are learned behaviours different from instincts?

14 Sai was born blind in one eye. The eye was fixed when she was 6 months old, but she never learned to use it. Suggest a reason for this.

15 Some politicians argue that we should spend less on schools and more on helping mothers to care for their babies. What evidence could they use to support their case?

Get this

- We inherit instincts but most of our behaviour is learned.
- Learned behaviour is influenced by rewards, punishments and imitating other people.
- Neglected babies can have learning and behavioural problems later.

How science works

Fever

Abha has a fever. She caught malaria when a mosquito bit her. It happens to millions of people every year. At least 1 million die because they can't afford medicines.

 1 Why are mosquito nets important in countries where malaria is common?

2 Why do so many people die of malaria?

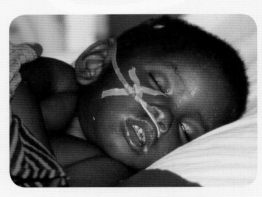

There used to be some affordable drugs which could kill most malaria microbes. A few **microbes** had genes which stopped the drug affecting them. These **resistant** microbes survived, reproduced and passed on their genes. Now, most malaria microbes have them, and the old drugs no longer work.

The best cure for malaria now is an expensive chemical called artemisinin. Chinese herbalists have used *Artemisia* plants to make it for thousands of years. Specialist cells on their leaves make the artemisinin. It is expensive to extract the pure chemical from the plant and it is too complicated to make in a lab.

To stop resistance to artemisinin developing, it is mixed with other chemicals to make ACT. Microbes rarely develop resistance to more than one chemical at once, so there should always be a cure for those who can afford it.

3 Explain why artemisinin is so expensive.

4 Artemisinin will cure malaria by itself. Why mix it with other chemicals?

▲ An Artemisia plant leaf

Stamping out malaria

The companies that make medicines can't cure malaria by themselves. It costs billions, and most malaria victims are too poor to pay.

In 2003, the Bill & Melinda Gates Foundation published 'Grand Challenges in Global Health' and began to fund research to find better treatments.

Since 2005 there has been an international strategy for tackling the disease funded by governments and charities all over the world.

 5 Match each of the 'grand challenges' to one of these ways of reducing deaths from malaria: reduce the number exposed to the microbe, increase their immunity, provide better medicines and make sure the medicines don't stop working?

6 Explain why governments and charities need to pay for malaria treatments.

Grand challenges
for improving health in developing nations

Improve vaccines
Develop new vaccines
Control insects
Improve nutrition
Limit resistance
Cure infections
Measure health

Selection

Scientists are trying to make artemisinin cheaper by breeding plants which make more of it, that is, have higher **yields**.

UK scientists checked 25,000 plants. Their yield showed **continuous variation**, but a few plants produced much more artemisinin than the rest.

By breeding different plants with the high yields together, we can get new plants with the highest possible yield. This is **selective breeding**.

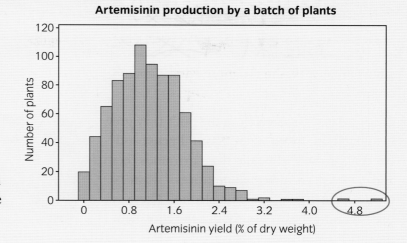

Artemisinin production by a batch of plants

Number of plants / Artemisinin yield (% of dry weight)

7 What is continuous variation?

8 What was the most common yield?

9 What was the highest yield in this batch?

Synthetic biology

Other scientists are trying a different tactic. They are using **genetic engineering**.

The genes other species use to make useful chemicals can be added to bacteria or yeast cells. They make these microbes produce the chemical. Insulin has been produced like this for many years.

Microbes reproduce quickly, and the chemicals are cheaper to extract from microbes.

Scientists hope to produce artemisinin for a much lower price so that all malaria victims can afford it.

10 What does genetic engineering involve?

11 What advantages does the technique offer?

Summing up

12 Malaria was wiped out in the US many years ago. Give two reasons why it is more difficult to do the same thing in Africa.

13 Suggest why wiping out the disease will require international collaboration.

14 How will the genetically-engineered product help to eradicate malaria?

Get this

- In most species there are a few organisms with genes which resist medicines.
- Selective breeding and genetic engineering can produce affordable treatments quickly.

Living factories

Microbe magic

Did you know that making chocolate depends on microbes?

Cacao beans are taken from the pods they grew in and left out in the open. Natural **yeast** and **bacteria** grow in the pulp that surrounds them and excrete a complicated mixture of waste products, including acid and alcohol. These react with the beans to produce the chocolate flavour.

After 5 days' treatment the beans are dried and sold.

1 Acid and alcohol develop the chocolate flavours in cacao beans. How do they get into the mixture?

Learn about
● Using microbes

Fake spiders

Scientists think we could get microbes to make nearly everything we need by adding new genes to them.

This spider's silk could make ultra light fabrics with amazing strength and elasticity. It is far better than manufactured silk, but we can't get enough of it.

Spiders tend to eat each other if many are kept together, so scientists put their silk-making genes in bacteria. Silk is toxic to most bacterial cells, but *Salmonella* bacteria can make it and survive.

Salmonella causes food poisoning in humans. Its cells have tiny miniature syringes in their walls which they use to inject our gut cells with toxins. When forced to make silk, they use their syringes to throw the silk out as fast as they make it. So the bacteria are unharmed and the silk is collected easily.

2 What useful properties does spiders' silk have?

3 Genetic engineers usually add new genes to *E. coli* bacteria or yeast cells. Why choose *Salmonella* to make silk?

BioBricks™

BioBrick™ parts can give microbes new features. Some 'bricks' are single genes; others are collections of genes that work together.

Controlling what microbes do is called synthetic biology and it's a difficult thing to do. Different labs work with different genes. But scientists can build on each other's work by sharing BioBricks™. They all fit together like the parts in an electrical circuit. The vials in the picture contain different Biobrick™ parts.

 4 What are BioBrick™ parts?

5 How could BioBrick™ parts speed up progress in synthetic biology?

What if?

Cleaning up oil spills used to be very hard work. Scientists have found bacteria that can do the job. **Genetically modified** microbes might clear up other pollutants.

Most modified microbes could be kept safely indoors, but to clear up pollution they'd need to be released. Could safe microbes mutate and become harmful in the outside world? Scientists think it's unlikely but not impossible, so safety regulations need to be put in place.

 6 Give one reason why modified microbes might be released into the environment?

7 What concerns might people have about this?

Learning from the past

When genetically modified (GM) food crops were developed, it was difficult for members of the public to obtain unbiased information about them. Many people in the UK were suspicious. They fought to keep GM crops out of the country, and have so far succeeded.

Scientists modifying microbes plan to work with social scientists who will keep the public informed and involve them in decision making.

 8 Why is it important that everyone should know how scientists are modifying microbes?

Summing up

9 Humans have used microbial waste products for thousands of years to make products like chocolate, bread and alcohol. What is different about the way microbes are used now?

10 Suggest why regulations need to be put in place to control the modification of microbes.

Get this

- Microbes can be genetically modified to make new products.
- Scientists need to address safety concerns about modified microbes.

2.1 Strength

Lift

Xiexia Chen pushed 2½ times her body weight above her head to win an Olympic gold medal.

Trained muscles like hers can exert huge forces, but they can't push. To swing the weights into position her muscles contract, get shorter, and pull on **tendons** attached to bones. As she bends and straightens her arms and legs, the weights are jerked upwards.

 1 How do muscles cause movement?

The muscles that move our bones work in pairs. One pulls a bone one way and its partner reverses the movement. They are **antagonistic**, which means they work against each other. When one **contracts** the other **relaxes**.

The muscle that works against gravity is always bigger.

 2 Why are the muscles in your upper arm called antagonistic muscles?

3 Hold your hand palm upwards. Which muscle is bigger – the one at the front of your upper arm or the one at the back? Explain why.

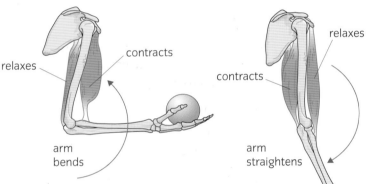

relaxes · contracts · arm bends · relaxes · contracts · arm straightens

Shocked

When Troy got hit by lightning on his school sports field, it burnt through his helmet and blew off his shoes (shown in the picture). His breathing stopped but was restarted. He was lucky to survive without major damage. Lightning strike victims often break several bones.

Muscles are controlled by messages from nerves. They normally take turns to contract. But lightning makes every muscle cell pull at once – suddenly and violently.

When antagonistic pairs both pull at once, they can break your bones. But the muscles in each pair aren't equal in strength. The strongest ones jerk your bones. They can make you leap several metres and then land with a crash.

 4 How is muscle contraction controlled?

5 Why can a bolt of lightning make you jump much further than you normally can?

Saved

Lisa didn't think when she saw a boy trapped under a car. She heaved the wheels clear of his legs so bystanders could pull him out.

When your sense organs detect an emergency, your brain reacts instantly. It uses a chemical called adrenalin to increase the blood supply to your muscles, make your heart and lungs work harder and pour **glucose** into your blood. This lets muscles release more energy and pull harder if they need to. For just a few seconds, you can have superhuman strength.

6 Why does extra glucose and oxygen let muscles pull harder?

7 How does your body get extra blood to muscles in an emergency?

Superhuman

Simon needs to be strong. Fire fighting equipment is heavy and he has to drag unconscious adults out of burning buildings. But lifting heavy weights tires his muscle cells. He can only do it for a short time. Then his muscles need to rest and repair themselves.

A robotic exoskeleton would give Simon extra strength. It uses sensors to detect the nerve impulses we send to our muscles. These control the exoskeleton's motors too. So it can copy every move the wearer makes, but with twenty times the strength.

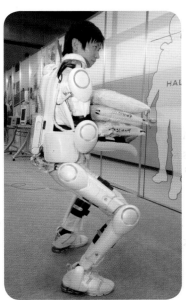

Scientists hope modified exoskeletons will help people whose nerves are damaged walk automatically.

8 How does the robotic exoskeleton mimic its wearer's actions?

9 Why are people with nerve damage often unable to walk?

Summing up

10 Why are two sets of muscles needed to bend and straighten your knee?

11 Explain why weight lifters need a high energy intake.

12 Why might a nurse with disabled patients find a robotic exoskeleton useful?

Get this

- Muscles work in antagonistic pairs to move bones.
- Electric shocks or stress can make muscle contractions bigger.

Dance

Maya loves to dance. It's exciting. But her explosive jumps, hard landings and sudden changes of direction put extreme force on her joints. She has to train carefully to avoid serious injury.

Joints need to be strong enough to hold our bones together and flexible enough to let them move. Our knee and elbow joints work like hinges to let our legs and arms bend and straighten. Shoulder and hip joints are more like joysticks. They let our arms and legs rotate. Most other joints have less flexibility. The bones just slide against each other.

1 Why do dancers get a lot of joint injuries?

2 Which joints give your bones most freedom of movement?

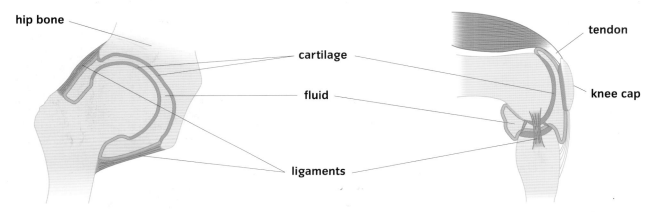

hip bone · cartilage · fluid · ligaments · tendon · knee cap

Injury

Like dancers, professional footballers need a lot of agility. Their speed and direction keep changing as the ball shoots round the pitch.

A bad tackle made Carl twist his knee yesterday. Now it is swollen and painful. He has sprained it, which means he has damaged one of the **ligaments** around the joint. He used ice to reduce the swelling but needs to rest until the joint repairs itself.

Ligaments hold bones together so they need to resist pulling forces. Knee ligaments stretch enough to let your leg bend and straighten, but they can tear or break if the knee joint twists. Major damage takes months to heal.

3 Why do ligaments need to be strong but slightly stretchy?

4 Footballers often suffer from sprains. What causes them?

5 What should you do to reduce the damage if you sprain a ligament?

Smooth running

Doris has been for an X-ray. She used to be very active but now she can hardly walk. Moving her legs is just too painful. It's hard to see where her leg bones end and her hip bone begins on the X-ray. Doris has severe arthritis.

Normally, the ends of our bones are covered with a layer of **cartilage**. This strong, smooth tissue lets our bones slide over each other smoothly, and fluid in our joints keeps it lubricated. Cartilage also gives a little. It absorbs some of the force when our legs hit the ground, so the ends of our bones don't crack against each other.

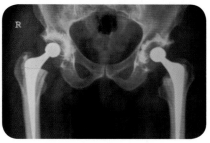

Doris has bare bone where the cartilage should be. The cartilage has broken down. There is a lot of friction in her joints and every movement hurts.

 6 Draw a diagram of a hip joint to show where there should be cartilage.

New parts

Doris's new X-ray looks completely different. She's had her hip joints replaced. Surgeons sawed off the ends of her leg bones. They fixed tough metal balls to the cut ends and stuck smooth non-stick sockets to her hip bones. Now she can move without pain.

Hip replacement surgery is expensive and hospitals are always short of money. Some won't do the operation on people who are obese or very old. They say they cannot afford to treat everyone, so younger people should take priority.

 7 Do you agree with hospitals who refuse to perform hip operations on very old people? Give your reasons.

Summing up

8 Say whether these descriptions apply to cartilage, bone or ligament, or a combination of the three: strong when squashed; strong when pulled; rigid; flexible; smooth?

9 Explain why ligaments and cartilage need different properties.

10 The number of older people in the UK is increasing. Why might that cause problems for health care providers?

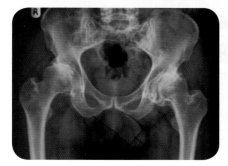

Get this

- Joints let muscles move bones.
- Ligaments hold the bones together and cartilage stops them rubbing against each other.

Learn about
- Maintaining energy supplies

Race

Kenyan Martin Lel wins marathons. He has **stamina**, which means he can run for hours. The key to his success is fast **respiration**.

Respiration releases energy from glucose and **oxygen**, and that keeps cells alive. Martin's muscles use this energy to contract when he runs.

glucose + oxygen → **respiration** → carbon dioxide + water

energy

Glucose and oxygen **diffuse** into cells as fast they get used up, as long as there is enough in the blood.

1 Name the reaction that releases energy inside cells?

2 Why do runners often sip glucose drinks?

Oxygen

Martin is very fit, which means his heart and lungs work efficiently and let his blood pick up oxygen quickly.

Blood makes most tissues look red in real life, but this model uses colour to make the **circulatory system** clearer.

Blood in the red side of your heart is full of oxygen. This side pumps hard. Blood shoots through the red **arteries** to every corner of your body.

The blue veins bring blood back so the blue side can push it through your lungs to pick up oxygen. Then a vein hidden from view carries it back to the heart.

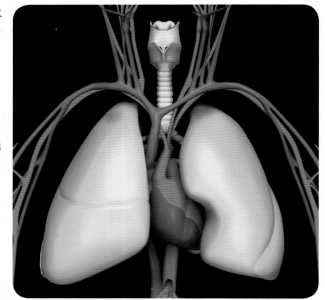

When Martin runs a race, he breathes faster and deeper, pumps more blood around and takes in oxygen more quickly.

3 Why does blood pass through your heart twice on each trip round the body?

4 Which side of Martin's heart sends oxygen-rich blood to his muscles?

5 Explain two things Martin's body does to move oxygen into his blood faster.

Blood

Your heart can make blood circulate five times faster, but that's not enough to keep you running. So **blood vessels** alter your blood's circulation to match each tissue's need. The chart shows what happened when one athlete started to jog.

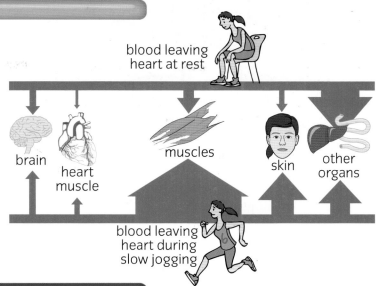

blood leaving heart at rest

brain

heart muscle

muscles

skin

other organs

blood leaving heart during slow jogging

 6 What happened to the amount of blood leaving her heart?

7 Which organs got more blood when she started to jog?

8 Which organ's blood supply didn't change?

Fuel

Martin eats starchy **carbohydrates** – such as pasta – the day before a race. They break down to glucose in his digestive system. Glucose is a soluble carbohydrate, so his blood can carry it around and it can get into cells.

His muscles and liver cells store enough carbohydrate to run nearly half a marathon. Any extra is taken in by fat cells and converted to fat.

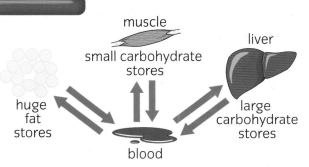

muscle

small carbohydrate stores

liver

huge fat stores

large carbohydrate stores

blood

tiny amounts of glucose and fat in blood

 9 How does your body store most of its energy supplies?

10 Where are carbohydrates stored?

As Martin runs, his muscles use their carbohydrates, and take glucose and fat from his blood. Liver and fat cells keep his blood topped up.

The graph shows how long his carbohydrates last. The fat stores last longer. But muscles can't work hard when fat is their only energy source, so Martin has to make his carbohydrates last. He can't run as fast as a 1500 m runner.

stored carbohydrate (%)

long walk

marathon run

1500 m race

Exercise time (min)

 11 Why do Martin's liver and fat cells need to keep topping up his blood?

12 Why does a 1500 m runner use their carbohydrates up faster than a marathon runner?

Summing up

13 Why is respiration important to athletes?

14 Why can fit people run faster?

15 Distance runners consume glucose during a race. Why is it the most suitable energy source?

Get this

- Marathon runners have stamina.
- Their muscles can **respire** at the fastest possible rate because their bodies keep their blood topped up with glucose and oxygen.

Fast

Learn about
- Anaerobic respiration

Usain Bolt is fast. He grabbed three Gold medals in the 2008 Olympics.

Marathon runners average 6 m/s, but Usain's average speed was more than 10 m/s, and he didn't take a breath until he crossed the finish line. His muscles had to manage without extra oxygen. So how did they contract enough to move him so fast?

No-one could beat Usain over 100 or 200 m, but could he win a marathon like Martin Lel? Sports scientists look for answers by studying runners' muscles.

1 List two differences between the races that earned gold medals for Martin Lel and Usain Bolt.

2 Which observation suggests something is different about the way the athletes' muscles release energy?

Muscle

If you cut up a roast chicken you find two sorts of meat, the light meat on the breast and the darker meat on the legs. The meat looks different because it contains different types of muscle fibre. Humans have two main muscle types too. They are mixed together in your muscles, but they behave very differently.

Features	Muscle types	
	Slow twitch	Fast twitch
Colour	dark	light
Contraction speed	slow	fast
Endurance	high	low
Force produced	small	large
Capillaries	many	few

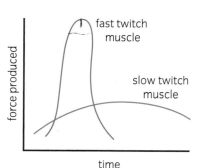

Athlete	Calf muscle (%)	
	slow	fast
marathon runner	79	21
100 m sprint runner	24	76
weight lifter	44	56

3 Which muscle type can exert most force?

4 Which muscle type can keep going for longer?

5 What evidence is there that the slow twitch fibres might take up oxygen faster?

6 What could account for a sprinter's faster speed?

7 Why would a sprinter's muscles be no use in a marathon?

Power stations

This microscope image shows a slice through a muscle cell. There's more than one **nucleus** and they're jammed against the **membrane**.

Dark orange filaments fill the **cytoplasm**. These use energy to make the muscle cell contract.

The round shapes between the filaments are **mitochondria**. Most respiration happens inside these.

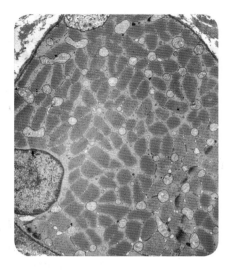

 8   Name the four components present in most cells.

9   What is unusual about the contents of a muscle cell?

Instant energy

When Martin runs a marathon he uses all his stored glucose for respiration. The process uses oxygen so it's called **aerobic respiration**. Martin's slow twitch muscles specialise in this.

Usain's race is over in ten seconds. He needs a lot of energy fast. His muscle cells store fuel but they can't store oxygen, and he can't wait for his blood to bring it.

When muscles work hard for less than two minutes they get most of their energy from **anaerobic respiration**. This doesn't need oxygen. It only releases 5% of the energy in glucose, compared to 100% in aerobic respiration, but cells can use a lot of glucose at once. So 5% of its total energy is a lot. Usain's fast twitch muscles specialise in anaerobic respiration, but all runners use it when they start running, or make a dash for the finish line.

 10   Make a table to summarise the differences between aerobic and anaerobic respiration.

Anaerobic respiration has one disadvantage. It makes lactic acid instead of carbon dioxide and this is toxic if it builds up. So anaerobic respiration can't carry on at full speed for more than a couple of minutes.

When a runner stops, they carry on breathing fast. The extra oxygen removes lactic acid and helps the muscles recover.

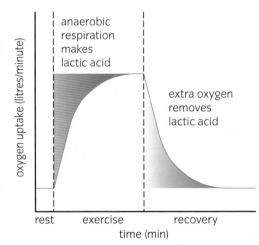

anaerobic respiration makes lactic acid

extra oxygen removes lactic acid

oxygen uptake (litres/minute)

rest   exercise   recovery
time (min)

Summing up

11   Cheetahs are the fastest animals on land. What sort of fibre would you expect to find in their leg muscles?

12   Why can't cheetahs chase their prey for very long?

13   Why do heart muscle cells have a lot of mitochondria?

14   Why is anaerobic respiration so useful?

Get this

- Most respiration uses oxygen, so it is aerobic. It happens in mitochondria.
- Fast twitch muscles can use anaerobic respiration. It releases energy faster, but not for long.

Keeping cool

Hot

Jasmine loves to dance but it always makes her sweat.

As her muscle cells respire faster to give her energy to move, they also release more heat. Her blood warms up as it runs past them and spreads that heat all over her body.

Your blood temperature is normally 37 °C. Skin acts like an air conditioner to keep it steady. Sensors in your brain check for any rise or fall in temperature. If they detect a change, your brain takes action. It sends nerve messages to your skin to bring it back to normal.

 1 Why do we get hot when we exercise?

2 How do our bodies stay the same temperature all over?

Glowing

Your skin glows when you exercise because its blood vessels open up. They let more blood flow close to the surface, where it loses heat to the cooler air around you. You also produce sweat. This absorbs heat from your skin as it evaporates, so it makes you cool down faster. But you can lose a lot of water on a hot day.

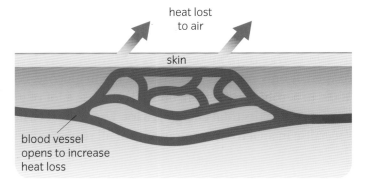

heat lost to air

skin

blood vessel opens to increase heat loss

 3 Jasmine's face is glowing. Why does this happen when she exercises?

4 How does sweating cool you down?

Heat can only be conducted from a hotter material to a colder material. So when your surroundings are warmer than 37 °C, you can only cool your body by sweating.

Saunas like this one are heated to between 70 °C and 90 °C. People are advised not to spend more than 20 minutes inside at a time. The steamier it is, the slower sweat evaporates and the harder it is to stay cool.

 5 Even in the UK, air temperatures can rise above 37 °C in summer. Why is sweating essential in these conditions?

6 People often feel thirsty after a sauna. Explain why.

Adaptation

Runners 6 and 12 are from kenya. They are taller and thinner than average. That's an advantage during a marathon. They can lose heat faster because they have a bigger skin area to lose it from.

Runner number 1 is from China. Her body's smaller surface area makes it easier to stop heat escaping during colder periods.

 7 When is it an advantage to have a large area surface area of skin?

8 Long distance runners need to lose heat fast to avoid overheating. What sort of body shape would you expect them to have?

Dehydration

Mary is excited. It's her first marathon. She takes regular sips of water. It's a hot day, so she will sweat a lot. If she didn't replace the water she'd become dehydrated. She could get cramps, or collapse completely.

Sports scientists calculate an athlete's water loss by measuring how much their mass drops.

9 Study the graph. When the athlete lost 3% of their mass, how was their speed affected?

Danger

Laura is full of energy and on a high. She's taken ecstasy. It's a stimulant and **hallucinogen**. She's sweating, so she drinks lots of water to avoid dehydration. Back home, she falls asleep and never wakes up. She drank too much water.

If you drink too much, you normally produce more urine. But ecstasy can stop this happening. The extra water diluted Laura's blood too much. All her cells swelled up, her brain squashed against her skull, and she died.

Summing up

10 Why are brain cells the most likely to be damaged if they swell up?

11 What is your average body temperature?

12 How is does your skin help keep your temperature steady?

13 What can go wrong if you drink too much or too little?

Get this

- We sweat to lose heat and keep our blood at 37°C.
- Losing or gaining too much water can be dangerous.

2.6 Gasping for breath

Emergency

Jen heard a loud bang and felt air rush past her. The plane tipped forwards and started falling out of the air. That's the last thing she remembers.

Her plane was flying at 9000 metres – a little higher than Everest – when an explosion in the baggage hold blew a hole in its side. The air in the plane became the same as the air outside.

Air up here is thinner, so her breaths suddenly took less oxygen in. She panicked. Then she passed out.

The plane took a steep dive. It soon reached air that was safe to breath. Jen recovered once she was getting extra oxygen.

1 Why should you grab an oxygen mask if there's a hole in the side of your plane?

Thin air

Your lungs let gases diffuse between air and blood fast.

The air follows branching tubes into tiny **alveoli**. They look like bunches of hollow grapes with **capillaries** running around them. As red cells race through these, they pick up as much oxygen as they can carry.

But at the height of Everest it's a different story. A lungful of air at that height has less than half as many molecules as at sea level. Red cells leave your lungs half full, so oxygen diffuses into your tissues much more slowly.

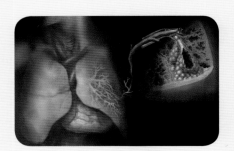

2 Draw one of the alveoli with a capillary running round it. Use a red arrow to show the direction of oxygen diffusion and a blue arrow for carbon dioxide.

3 Why do your tissues get less oxygen at high altitudes?

The death zone

Thousands have climbed Everest. Given time, your body adapts to low oxygen levels. It makes more red blood cells and grows extra capillaries in your muscles. But you still need extra oxygen to get you to the very top. Some people can't adapt. After a day at high altitudes, fluid fills their lungs. If they don't get down quickly they die.

Most climbers employ local people to carry their supplies. Their ancestors lived high up for many generations. Those with helpful genes were more likely to survive and pass them to their children. So most local people can cope with low oxygen levels now. Even so, no-one lives permanently above 5500 metres.

4 List two changes that take place when you spend time at high altitudes?

5 Can everyone adapt equally well?

 Keeping lungs fit

Your oxygen uptake also depends on the state of your lungs.

When you breathe, you take in microbes. These yellow bacteria won't cause trouble. They are trapped in strands of **mucus**. The waving hair-like **cilia** will sweep them up and out of your lungs.

But toxins in cigarette smoke paralyse these cilia, so dirt, microbes and mucus build up in your airways. That makes oxygen uptake slower, and infections more common.

6 Why do smokers get more lung infections?

Jackie has cystic fibrosis – an inherited disease. Her mucus is much thicker than normal so her cilia can't shift it. Carers must pound her chest to shake it free. Then she can cough it up.

Bacteria grow fast in Jackie's mucus. She's used **antibiotics** so often that her microbes are **resistant**. They are getting harder and harder to kill.

7 List two ways Jackie tries to keep bacteria out of her lungs?

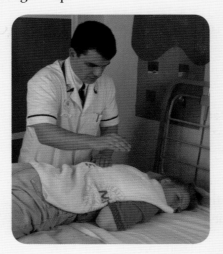

Summing up

8 Why is it harder to breath at the top of a mountain?

9 Why are athletes from high altitudes hard to beat?

10 Explain why smokers can't run far without getting out of breath?

11 Why do cystic fibrosis sufferers keep using new antibiotics?

Get this

- Oxygen diffuses into blood in alveoli in your lungs.
- Oxygen uptake drops at high altitudes and when your lungs are infected or clogged by mucus.

Learn about
- Circulation

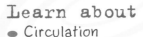

Landing

Astronauts have to pass tough selection tests. When these men left, they were some of the fittest men on Earth. Now they need help to get out of the capsule.

The trip has affected their circulatory systems. Their hearts are weaker and they feel dizzy when they stand up. It will be weeks before their bodies get back to normal.

 1 Which of the astronauts' body systems have been affected most by their time in space?

Weightless

When astronauts become weightless their legs shrink and their faces puff up – but why?

Your heart pumps blood into thick muscular arteries. These keep it under pressure, as it shoots off to your capillaries to deliver supplies to cells.

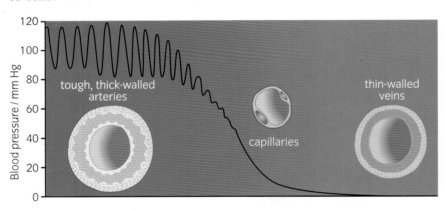

Blood pressure / mm Hg — tough, thick-walled arteries — capillaries — thin-walled veins

Blood drifts back to your heart through wide **veins** under low pressure. **Valves** keep it flowing in the right direction, but gravity keeps a lot of blood in your legs when you're standing up.

When astronauts are weightless, their blood spreads out evenly – so more goes to their heads. The change makes them feel as if their eyes are bulging out.

 2 Draw diagrams to show the differences between arteries, veins and capillaries.

3 Explain why you have three main types of blood vessel.

4 Why does blood need to flow through all your tissues?

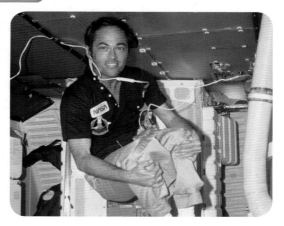

Making adjustments

As soon as he gets into space, Mike has to go to the toilet. Why?

Blood moving out of his legs makes his brain think he has too much. So it tells his kidneys to make more urine by taking water out of his blood.

The main components of blood are red cells and plasma. The watery plasma carries everything that dissolves well: carbon dioxide, **nutrients**, minerals, **hormones**, etc. Red cells just carry oxygen.

 5 Draw a diagram to show the main components of blood.

6 Add labels to show where oxygen and carbon dioxide are carried.

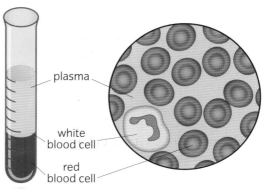

plasma

white blood cell

red blood cell

Mike's heart doesn't need to work so hard in space, so its muscles start to shrink and get weaker.

When he returns to Earth's gravity, blood will collect in his legs again. His heart will really struggle to push enough blood up to his brain, and if it's run short of oxygen he will faint.

 7 Explain why your heart works harder on Earth than it would in orbit.

8 Why might an astronaut faint when they try to stand up back on Earth?

Exercise

Your bodyweight puts huge forces on your bones here on Earth, and muscles must contract to hold you upright.

Astronauts on the space station can spend months in orbit. They hardly use their muscles, and the forces on their bones are tiny. So their muscles shrink and their bones become hollow and weak. They exercise for 4 hours a day, just to slow down the process.

 9 What happens to bones when there are no forces on them?

Summing up

10 Explain the effects lack of gravity has on the circulatory system.

11 What do your kidneys do if your body has too much fluid?

12 Explain why exercise is even more important in space than it is on Earth.

Get this

- Arteries carry blood from the heart at high pressures.
- Veins return blood at much lower pressures.
- Your muscles and bones get weaker if they aren't used.

Learn about
- Replacing organs

A new heart

Underneath the sheets is a tiny baby boy. The heart Liam was born with didn't work. He wasn't expected to survive.

Now tubes carry Liam's blood through a heart–lung machine, while surgeons stitch a crash victim's heart into his chest.

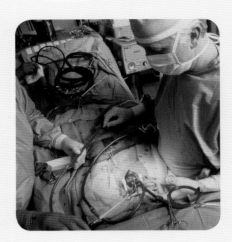

More than 80% of **transplant** patients survive, but Liam will need special medicines for the rest of his life. Otherwise his immune system will reject the new heart.

Only a fraction of the patients waiting for transplants get one in time to save their lives.

1 Many people on the transplant waiting list die each year? Suggest why.

2 Why do patients who get transplants always need to take medicines?

The gift of life

Karen's kidneys don't work, so she lies hooked to this machine for 3 hours at time, 3 times a week. It keeps her alive by clearing waste from her blood, but it isn't perfect. She has to stick to a special diet and will die early if she doesn't get a transplant.

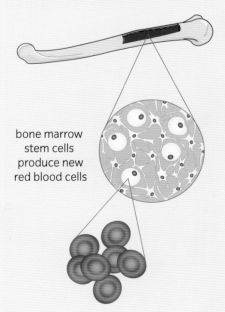

A **donor** kidney would need to be tissue matched – which means very like her own. Many patients' relatives give them a kidney. They know they can live a normal life with just one, and it's a fairly safe operation.

Other organ donations are more dangerous. You can give away enough liver or lung to keep someone else alive, but there's a high risk you'll suffer serious complications. So doctors may advise you not to do it.

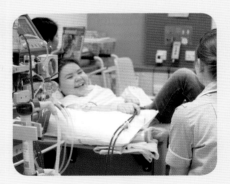

bone marrow stem cells produce new red blood cells

3 Give one reason why kidneys are transplanted more often than hearts.

4 Why might doctors advise against transplanting tissues from living donors?

Growing your own

If you give away part of your liver, the cells left behind keep dividing and it soon gets back to its original size. It's the only organ that can do this.

Red blood cells only last a few months but they can't replace themselves. Stem cells in your bone marrow keep making new ones. If stem cells could replace a whole organ, it would be perfect. Your body couldn't reject it.

The stem cells in your embryo eventually made all your cells, but the stem cells inside you now just make a few types each – and only when they pick up signals called **growth factors**.

5 Why would it be useful to build new organs from patients' stem cells?

6 How are red blood cells replaced when they wear out?

Recycling

The pink thing in the beaker is an artificial bladder. Scientists grew its cells around a shape called a **scaffold** - then took the scaffold away.

Scientists all over the world are growing stem cells on artificial scaffolds. But why not **recycle** a natural one?

Your nose, earlobes and windpipe use cartilage to keep their shape. Cartilage cells surround themselves with protein to make a stiff but flexible tissue called cartilage.

When Claudia needed a new windpipe, her doctors took one from a dead woman and washed all its cells away. So the only thing left was the protein, with gaps where the donor's cartilage cells used to be. When doctors added stem cells from Claudia's bone marrow, they used the protein as a scaffold and a whole new windpipe grew.

Now the race is on to make more complicated organs this way.

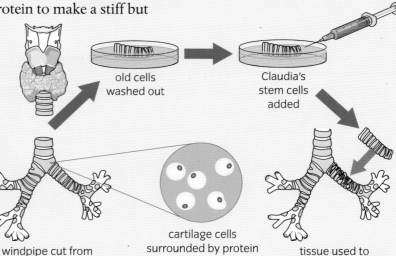

old cells washed out

Claudia's stem cells added

windpipe cut from dead woman

cartilage cells surrounded by protein

tissue used to fix Claudia's lungs

7 Why was it important to wash all the donor's cells away?

Summing up

8 How are embryonic stem cells different from adult stem cells?

9 Why are organs made from stem cells better than transplants?

10 How do scientists get stem cells to make the right shaped organ?

11 How do stem cells know when to start growing and dividing?

Get this

- Organs can be transplanted but medicines are needed to prevent rejection.
- New organs might be grown from stems cells in future.

Deaf blind

Jenny was born deaf and she'll slowly lose her sight. She has Usher's syndrome. One of her genes is faulty, so **sensory cells** in her eyes and ears don't work properly.

Everything you see, hear, taste, smell or feel, and everything you know about your body – like what your arms and legs are doing – depends on sensory cells.

Sensory cells are part of your **nervous system**. They specialise in detecting things. But your ears don't hear and your eyes don't see. They just send signals along nerves to your brain. Your brain processes these signals to make sounds and vision.

 1 What job are sensory cells specialised to do?

2 Why do most sensory cells send signals to your brain?

Bionic Hearing

The cells that detect sound are deep inside your ears in a snail-shaped **cochlea**. Your outer ear collects sounds and your middle ear makes the vibrations bigger. Then your sensory cells turn the vibrations into messages that can be sent to your brain.

Jenny's faulty sensory cells have been replaced by cochlear implants.

A microphone behind each ear collect sounds and transmits signals to a receiver under her skin. A wire from the receiver reaches deep inside her cochlea and stimulates the nerves that run from her ear to her brain.

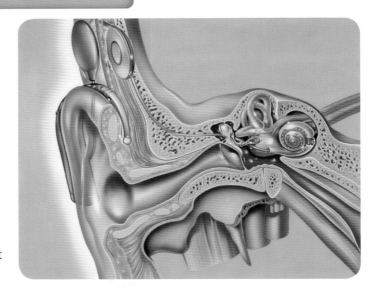

The sounds Jenny hears aren't very clear but she can usually make out what people are saying.

 3 Whereabouts in your ear are your sound-detecting cells?

4 What does the rest of your ear do?

5 Explain why cochlear implants don't help people with damaged nerves.

Bionic vision

Your ears have thousands of sensory cells, but there are more than 100 million in the **retina** at the back of each eye. There are two types - rods and cones.

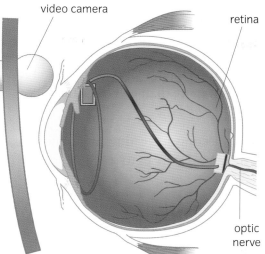

video camera

retina

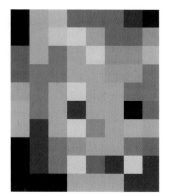

When Jenny goes blind she will have retinal implants fitted. Implants divide the retina into squares. A camera in Jenny's glasses will send signals to the nerves in each square, so her brain can work out what the camera is pointing at.

optic nerve

She hopes implants will get better before she goes blind. The image shows what she would see with one if she looked at her little brother's face with one of today's implants.

 6 Whereabouts in your eye are your light-detecting cells?

Energy detectors

Sound- and light-detecting cells look different, but they work in a similar way.

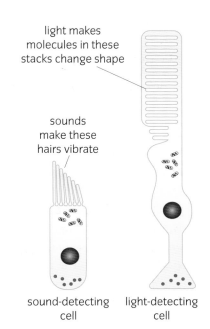

light makes molecules in these stacks change shape

sounds make these hairs vibrate

sound-detecting cell

light-detecting cell

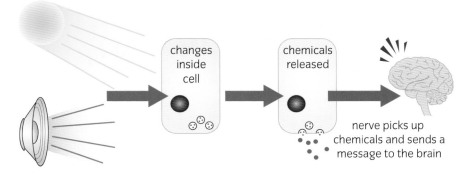

changes inside cell

chemicals released

nerve picks up chemicals and sends a message to the brain

Sound makes the hairs on sound-detecting cells vibrate, and light makes molecules inside light-detecting cells change shape. Then both cells release chemicals, which make nerves send out a signal.

 7 What is the same about the way hearing and vision work?

Summing up

8 List the five senses we use to monitor the world around us.

9 Make a flow chart to show what happens inside your body when you spot the lights of an approaching car.

10 In movies, bionic eyes and ears give people better hearing and vision. Is this realistic?

Get this

- Sensory cells detect things and send messages along nerves to your brain.
- Your brain processes nerve signals and makes you aware of what's happening.

Learn about
- Biodiversity

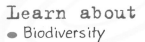

Forests

This small orang-utan has a big problem. His forest home covered Borneo for thousands of years, but more than half of its trees have been cut down recently.

Orang-utans spend their lives collecting and eating fruit – more than 300 different types. They travel huge distances to reach the right trees when their fruit is ready.

People cut down the trees to sell the wood and grow crops. Traditional farmers cultivate small patches for a year then move on, so the forest grows back. But modern farming removes the trees permanently.

 1 Why are orang-utans endangered on Borneo?

Biodiversity

Our orang-utan shares the remaining forest with rhinos, leopards, elephants, people, 700 other species of **vertebrates**, 15 000 species of plants and uncountable numbers of **invertebrate** species.

When many different **species** live in one place, we say it has a high **biodiversity**. Biodiversity is easy to lose and impossible to replace.

 2 What is biodiversity?

Plant heaven

The countries with the most biodiversity are all close to the equator. They receive more intense sunlight and get most rain, so **photosynthesis** takes place at the fastest possible rate.

Plants use photosynthesis to create new **biomass** and maintain Earth's oxygen supply, so it keeps every animal alive – including us.

We also take an extra share of the biomass to burn as fuel, feed farm animals, build homes and make clothing, paper and medicines.

 3 What two things does every animal rely on plants for?
4 What else do humans get from plants?

Strength in numbers

Scientists compared Borneo's rainforest with other hot, wet places. The chart shows what they found out.

Area	Biomass produced per year (in grams per m²)
rainforest	2500
grassland	1000
farmland	600

5 Which area produced most biomass per year?

6 Which area produced least biomass per year?

Each rainforest plant needs slightly different growing conditions. The tall trees grow fast to reach above the others. They need bright light.

The plants on the forest floor have darker leaves. They absorb the dim light that filters through the trees above them. So, between them, the forest plants use more of the sunlight. It's the same for every other resource such as water.

Places with high biodiversity can also recover quickly from setbacks. Pests and natural disasters are unlikely to wipe out every plant species, so natural forests can survive for thousands of years.

 7 Why is it an advantage to have many different species growing in the same place?

8 Why are rainforests less likely to be wiped out by disease than crop plants?

Biomass

Clouded leopards live and hunt in the treetops. They can snatch flying birds and monkeys out of the air or drop from the trees to ambush wild pigs and deer.

It takes a lot of forest to support one clouded leopard.

The herbivores in the forest use most of their food for respiration. A maximum of 10% is used to make new tissues such as muscle and bone. So the total biomass of herbivores is much less than the total biomass of plants. Clouded leopards use a small percentage of their food for growth too, so their total biomass is even lower.

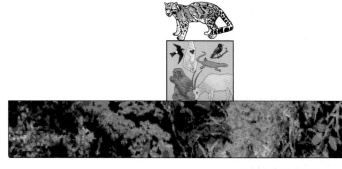

 9 Give two reasons why you are more likely to see a monkey or pig in the rainforest than a clouded leopard?

Summing up

10 Why do forests have a high biodiversity?

11 Give two reasons why it is good for a place to have a high biodiversity.

12 Why are forests that are thousands of years old now under threat?

13 Why does it take a lot of forest to support one clouded leopard?

Get this

- The biodiversity of an area is the number and variety of living things it contains.
- Forests have high biodiversity but deforestation threatens it.

Learn about
- Classification

A big cat?

Clouded leopards hunt alone – mainly at night – and spend most of their time in the treetops, so they are rarely seen close up. They roam Southern China as well as islands like Borneo. Their Chinese name means 'mint leopard' but the Malaysians on Borneo call them 'tree tigers'.

It's confusing when the same animal has several different names so scientists have a **classification** system. They sort animals into groups and subgroups according to their similarities and differences. Then give each species a unique two-part Latin name.

The first part of the name is the animal's smallest subgroup, and the second is their species name – which usually describes what's special about them.

1 How do scientists classify animals?

Classifying cats

The clouded leopard's fur and warm blood show it is a **mammal**. Its sharp claws, short skull, forward facing eyes and long canine teeth, prove it is a **carnivore** and it is a member of the cat family. But then its classification gets more difficult.

The cat family includes big cats that roar – lions, tigers, jaguars and leopards – and small cats that purr. Some so-called 'small cats', such as the puma, are actually quite large. Big cats and small cats also have differently shaped skulls and teeth.

The clouded leopard is less than half the size of an ordinary leopard. Its skull and teeth are shaped like a big cat's and it can roar, but it can also purr like a small cat. So scientists decided it was different enough to have its own subgroup – *Neofelis* – meaning 'new small cat'. Classification systems often have to change when a new species is discovered.

2 What features do all cats share?

3 Why did cat classification need to change when clouded leopards were discovered?

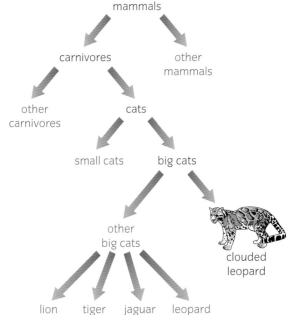

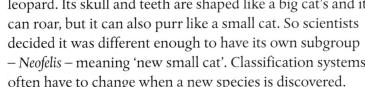

Proof

All species show a lot of **variation** so it is often difficult to decide whether two animals are the same species. If they are, they should be able to breed and their offspring should be **fertile**.

This animal is a liger – the offspring of a male lion and a female tiger. Its parents are from different species so the liger is a **hybrid**. Hybrids are usually infertile. They can't produce offspring of their own.

Unfortunately breeding experiments take a long time and animals won't always cooperate.

 4 Why is it difficult to tell whether or not animals belong to the same species?

5 How could you be sure that a male and female belonged to the same species?

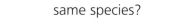
A new species

For a long while the clouded leopards on Borneo and mainland China shared the same scientific name – *Neofelis nebulosa*. But Borneo has been separate from the Chinese mainland for 300 000 years, so you would expect the leopards to have developed differently in each place during that time.

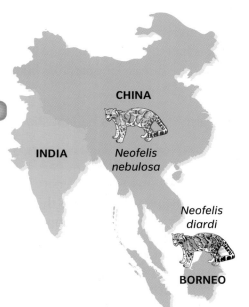

CHINA

INDIA

Neofelis nebulosa

Neofelis diardi

BORNEO

Scientists decided to check that the ones on Borneo were the same as the ones in China. They looked at the animal's genes. There were as many genetic differences between the two groups as there were between lions, tigers, leopards and jaguars. So the animals on Borneo became a separate species and were given a new name – *Neofelis diardi*.

Genetic evidence lets scientists check that they have only put closely related animals in the same subgroups.

6 Why did scientists think that clouded leopards weren't all the same species?

Get this

- Living things are classified into groups and subgroups with similar features.
- A group that can interbreed and produce fertile offspring is a species.
- Each species has a unique two-part scientific name.

Summing up

7 Why is it important for scientists all over the world to give each species the same name?

8 What is a species?

9 Why did many classification systems change when genetic evidence became available?

Facing extinction

Invaders

Sixty years ago the forests on Guam were full of birds. They began to disappear when brown tree snakes reached the island, hidden in a crate of supplies. Most of the island's birds are extinct now. The snakes ate them faster than they could reproduce.

With plenty of **prey** and no **predators**, snake numbers increased dramatically. Scientists found 8000 in one square kilometre of forest.

The place where a species lives is its **habitat**. It provides nutrients, water, space and shelter. In their original habitat, the snakes had to compete for food and also had predators. So starvation, disease or predators killed off most of their offspring.

 1 What is a habitat?

2 List four things a habitat should provide.

Interdependent

In habitats with low biodiversity – such as the arctic – a predator may rely on one prey. This makes the animals **interdependent**, which means that changes in the population of one animal affect the other animal's numbers.

As wolves eat caribou, the numbers of caribou drop. Then wolf numbers drop too because there are fewer caribou to feed them. Lower wolf numbers give the caribou a chance to breed, but as soon as their numbers increase, predator numbers start increasing too.

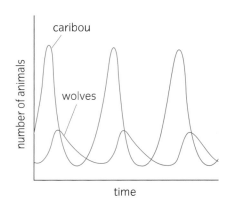

caribou

wolves

number of animals

time

 3 What would happen to the wolves if all the caribou were killed by hunters?

On Guam, there is more biodiversity. So when the number of birds dropped, the tree snakes started to eat rats, mice, lizards and bats. Meanwhile, the number of spiders rose dramatically because there were no birds to eat them.

4 The number of tree snakes carried on rising when the number of birds dropped. Explain why.

Endangered

When plants and animals share habitats, they often become interdependent. More than half of Guam's tree seeds were dispersed by birds. They ate the tree's fruit and dropped the seeds somewhere else in their faeces.

Now the seeds fall under the trees where they can't get enough light to grow. Scientists wonder if the forests will survive.

 5 Why is it important to disperse seeds?

Competition

This beetle is the size of a grain of rice, but a swarm of them can kill a huge pine tree in just two weeks. They only attack trees more than 80 years old.

Canada has always had pine beetles, but their **population** has exploded recently. Most of the trees in the forest are pine, but other trees grow between them. When trees get too crowded there is **competition** for space, water, carbon dioxide and light, so each tree does less photosynthesis and has less energy to grow.

The pines have an adaptation that helps them get rid of competitors. They only let their seeds drop when they have been heated by fire. The fire removes old trees and gives the seeds space to grow.

Pines compete with other species

Pine seeds survive forest fires

Young trees have no competition and old trees are rare

 6 What do trees compete for?

7 How does competition affect their growth?

Winners

Forest rangers do their best to stop fires, so there are more old trees than there used to be, and this creates a feast for the beetles.

Freezing winter weather used to kill most beetles, but climate change has made winters warmer, so most of the beetles survive. Their predators reproduce too slowly to eat the extra beetles.

 8 Explain why there are more pine beetles in Canada now.

Summing up

9 Why do most populations stay small even when many offspring are born?

10 What does it mean if animals are interdependent?

11 Suggest why an animal's population might suddenly increase.

Get this

- Populations are normally controlled by competition for food, predators and disease.
- Changes in a habitat such as new predators or human activity can make species extinct.

43

Learn about
- Biofuels

Green fuel?

These vehicles all run on petrol, or diesel, made from oil. But oil is non-renewable, and it's running out fast, so **biofuels** have become more popular.

Biofuels are made from plants, so they produce a crop every year. This means they are renewable. They can be replaced as fast as they are used.

Petrol and diesel release carbon dioxide as they burn. Biofuels also release carbon dioxide but the next crop of biofuels takes carbon dioxide out of the air again in photosynthesis. The diagram shows how these crops recycle carbon dioxide.

There are two main biofuels, **biodiesel** and **bioethanol**. Biodiesel is made from plant oils and bioethanol is made from sugars.

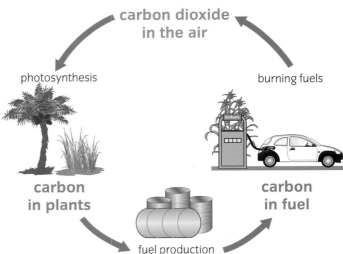

1 What are biofuels?

2 Why should biofuels add less carbon dioxide to the air than petrol?

Hidden costs

These oil palms grow on Borneo where there used to be rain forest.

Traditional farmers grow food for their families and local markets, but modern farmers sell their crops all over the world. The forest's main crop is its wood.

Once the forest has been cut down, the tropical conditions are perfect for growing palm oil. You may not remember eating it, but palm oil is in 1 in 10 supermarket items, including crisps and bread. Now it is being used for biofuels too.

As the forest disappears, species lose their habitats and die out, so biodiversity is lost for ever.

3 Why are modern farmers clearing more forest?

4 Why is there such a big demand for palm oil?

Releasing carbon dioxide

This fire was started deliberately. Clearing away the forest releases huge amounts of carbon dioxide.

Farmers will grow oil palms on the land. But these will take less carbon dioxide in than the massive trees in the forest did. The extra will stay in the air.

It can take more energy to produce biofuels than petrol because the process is more complex. Most of the energy comes from burning fuels, which releases carbon dioxide, so switching to biofuels can increase the amount of carbon dioxide in the atmosphere.

If farmers grow biofuel crops instead of food crops, they don't need to cut down the forest. But they can cause food shortages and price rises.

 5 List three ways biofuel production increases carbon dioxide levels.

6 What problems does it cause when biofuels replace food crops?

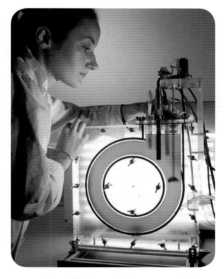

High tech biofuels

Algae grow fast, and oil can make up 60% of their biomass. They could use carbon dioxide from power stations to help them grow faster. Huge ponds would be needed to grow enough in sunlight to produce biodiesel, so scientists and engineers are trying to grow them in artificial light.

7 What would be the advantages of making biodiesel like this?

8 Suggest some drawbacks.

Up to 20% of sugar cane or beet plants is sugar, which can be used to make bioethanol. If all a plant's biomass could be turned into sugar, it could all be used. But plant cell walls are tough and only a few decomposers can break them down.

You can't see most of this fungus. It's inside the tree feeding. Its **enzymes** turn wood into a sugary mush. If we could harness these enzymes we could turn any waste plant material into bioethanol.

 9 Why can't the whole of a sugar beet be turned into bioethanol?

Summing up

10 Give two reasons for using biofuels instead of petrol?

11 Give two reasons for not using forest land to grow biofuels?

12 How could you make more biodiesel or bioethanol from the same mass of plant material?

Get this

- Biofuels are renewable and make less carbon dioxide than petrol or diesel.
- Making biofuel can do unintended damage to the environment.

45

3.5 Mangroves

Learn about
● Energy transfer in food webs

Drowned forests

These strange trees grow right at the edge of the sea along sheltered tropical coasts – they are mangroves. All mangrove trees have some of their roots above ground. When the tide comes in, it covers them with salty water, which would kill most plants.

A mangrove forest can contain many different tree species. They produce biomass as fast as tropical rainforests.

A huge variety of life lives in them and hundreds of other species use them as breeding grounds and nurseries for their offspring.

Local people get building materials, fuel, medicines and food from the mangroves, and the surrounding waters are rich fishing grounds.

1 Why are mangrove forests so important to local people?

2 Why are they important to the Earth as a whole?

Food chains

On land, most plants are eaten by herbivores. In mangroves, most leaves eventually fall into the water where bacteria and **fungi** can break them down. Organisms which release energy by breaking down dead plants or animals are **decomposers**.

Many different invertebrates feed on decomposers, and are eaten by carnivores, so mangrove forests have a high biodiversity and support complicated food webs.

3 Name two sorts of decomposer.

4 Most of the food chains in the mangroves depend on decomposers. Explain why.

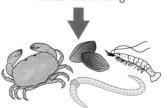

mangrove tree

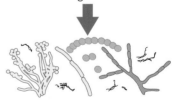

bacteria and fungi

invertebrates

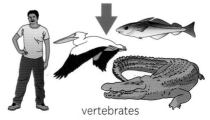

vertebrates

Limiting factors

Plants need light, water, carbon dioxide, minerals and a suitable temperature. If any of these is in short supply, photosynthesis slows down.

Most parts of the ocean are short of minerals. Tiny plants called **phytoplankton** take

▲ Mangrove forests

minerals from the water and get eaten by microscopic animals. When these die, they fall to the bottom and take the minerals with them.

Mangrove forests have high rates of photosynthesis because rivers bring minerals down to the shore, and tides stir them up from the seabed.

 5 List four things that can slow photosynthesis down.

6 Which is most likely to be missing from the oceans?

Oxygen

Oxygen for respiration can enter a plant's leaves from the air, or come from photosynthesis which happens in the **chloroplasts** during daylight. But all a plant's cells need some oxygen for respiration, including the root cells.

Roots usually get oxygen from the spaces between soil particles, so they die in waterlogged ground. But mangrove roots can take oxygen from air when the tide is low. They can also store enough in their spongy tissues to last while they are covered with water at high tide.

 7 How do mangrove roots respire when they are underwater?

Recycling

Mangrove forests transfer energy along food chains, but they recycle raw materials such as carbon. Plants take it out of the air as carbon dioxide. The carbon compounds they make are either used for respiration or passed to the next link in their food chain. Each consumer does the same thing with the carbon compounds in their food.

If a plant or animal avoids being eaten, it is broken down by decomposers after it dies.

 8 Decomposers take in carbon compounds from rotting leaves. Suggest two ways the carbon in these could get back into the air?

Summing up

9 How do decomposers get their energy?

10 Why do phytoplankton grow faster in shallow coastal waters?

11 Why do plants release more carbon dioxide during the night than they take in?

12 Explain why life on Earth couldn't continue if there were no decomposers.

Get this

- Decomposers use dead plants and animals to release energy and so recycle their raw materials.
- Carbon is recycled through food webs.

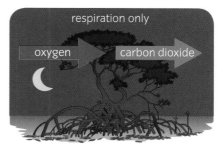
respiration only
oxygen → carbon dioxide

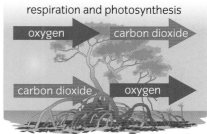
respiration and photosynthesis
oxygen → carbon dioxide
carbon dioxide → oxygen

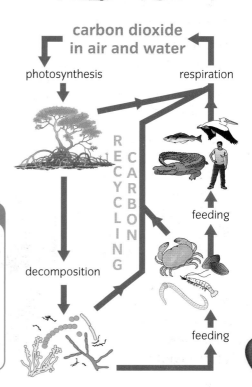
carbon dioxide in air and water
photosynthesis
respiration
RECYCLING CARBON
decomposition
feeding
feeding

Learn about
- Sustainability

Gain and loss

Fifteen thousand years ago, most of the UK was covered in ice and the rest was cold, dry and treeless. As the last ice age ended, it got warmer and wetter. Trees moved in, and one massive forest covered the whole of the UK.

1 Why was the UK treeless 15 000 years ago?

Of course, trees can't actually move, but wind, water and animals spread their seeds. When climate change makes a new area right for a species, the seeds that land there grow into trees and the forest spreads in that direction.

2 How did trees spread across the UK?

3 What decides where trees will survive?

Clues from the past

How do we know where trees grew in the past?

These scientists are drilling out thin columns of soil. The deeper the soil the older it is.

Each type of tree has different pollen, so by studying each layer they can tell what sort of trees grew here at different times in the past.

The evidence shows that forests once spread across Europe at about 100 m per year as the climate changed.

4 How can scientists tell what grew thousands of years ago?

Humans followed the trees as they moved into the UK. Six thousand years ago they began to cut them down. They used the wood for fuel or building, or to make more space for growing crops.

By 500 BC, half the forest had been burned or cut down. Now trees only cover around 12% of the land – mostly in tiny patches.

5 When did the UK's forests start to disappear?

6 Why were they removed?

Reforestation

As the forests disappeared, species such as wolves, bears, wild pigs and beavers lost their habitat and became extinct. So our countryside has been made what it is by people.

Now things are changing. Trees are being planted all over the UK, and a new National Forest is appearing right in the centre of England.

Trees will cover a third of the area by surrounding existing towns and villages, and growing on disused industrial land such as coal mines.

This **reforestation** uses a mixture of species to create different environments. Its major **environmental** benefit is that it helps maintain biodiversity.

 7   How can reforestation occur without moving people?

8   Why is it important to use a mixture of species?

Sustainability

The new forests must be **sustainable**, which means they will meet our current needs and conserve resources for future generations.

In the past, large carnivores such as wolves controlled herbivore populations in forests, so their populations never got high enough to destroy the vegetation. Now these are extinct, forests need to be conserved by humans.

Forests can provide a lot of work. They encourage tourists to spend money in the area and employ people to harvest timber for sale. So they can bring **economic** benefits to local people.

Quiet green spaces are very relaxing and the new forests also have adventure playgrounds and assault courses. So the forest has social benefits as well.

 9   Why are carnivores important to forests?

10   How can trees be harvested sustainably?

Summing up

11   List two things that affect the number of trees in an area?

12   Why does animal biodiversity drop when forests are removed?

13   What does reforestation involve?

14   What sort of benefits does reforestation bring to an area?

15   List three types of benefit reforestation can bring.

16   What makes a new development sustainable?

Get this

- Biodiversity can be maintained by preserving habitats.
- Sustainable development means meeting our current needs and conserving resources for future generations.

Flower power

When the Chernobyl nuclear reactor exploded, clouds of radioactive particles flew into the air. Large amounts of radioactivity can kill or cause serious health problems.

The highest levels of radiation were in the lakes and forests close to the site of the accident. They were **contaminated** with a radioactive metal called uranium.

Scientist turned to plants to clean up the water. They floated rafts of sunflowers on top of the lakes and waited. The plants pulled radioactive uranium into their leaves so it could be taken away and buried.

Concentrating pollutants like this is called **bioaccumulation**.

? **1** Why is it important to remove radioactivity from water?

Learn about
● How plants use water and minerals

Minerals

Plants have a natural ability to absorb **minerals**.

They need minerals, and glucose, to build their cells. The most useful ones are **nitrates** (containing nitrogen), **phosphates** (containing phosphorus) and **potassium**. They also need minute amounts of other metals, but not too much. Many metal compounds can be harmful.

metals spread through a large volume of soil

bioaccumulation in the plant's leaves

A few plants have adapted to survive in soils that would kill other plants. The soils contain compounds of metals that are usually harmful, such as copper, zinc, lead, cadmium or arsenic.

The plants absorb a lot of the metal, but it doesn't harm them. If we burn the plants, the metals from a huge amount of soil are left in a tiny quantity of ash.

? **2** Why do some metals need to be removed from soil?

Uptake

Plants take in metals through their roots but accumulate them in their leaves. How?

Roots take minerals in with the water they absorb through their **root hairs**. The water moves up to their leaves, through tubes called **xylem**

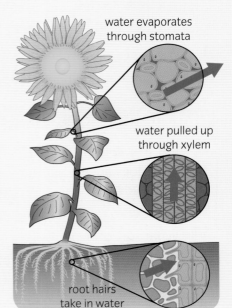
water evaporates through stomata

water pulled up through xylem

root hairs take in water

vessels in the stem. Any water its leaf cells don't need, evaporates through tiny gaps called **stomata** on the undersides of its leaves.

 3   Explain how minerals get into plants.

Storage

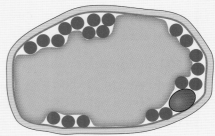

When a cell has enough water, its **vacuole** presses against the **cell wall** and keeps the cell firm, so plant tissues can support themselves.

Leaves use water for photosynthesis, so they need to keep replacing it. The water carries minerals into each cell. They are stored in the vacuole until they are needed, and that's where most toxic metals end up.

 4   What happens to plant cells if they don't have enough water to fill their vacuoles?

Poison?

Locusts like this have enormous appetites. They can form huge swarms containing more than a billion insects. As these sweep across the countryside they eat every green leaf.

We have insecticide sprays that can control them now, but locusts used to cause famines, especially in Africa and China.

These Chinese plants have a taste for arsenic, which is a very poisonous element. The concentration in their leaves is 100 times higher than in the soil.

Scientists thought the arsenic might stop locusts eating their leaves. When they offered the fern to hungry locusts they got these results.

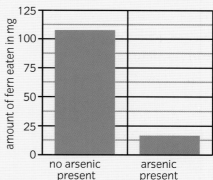

 5   What theory was the experiment designed to test?

6   Did the experiment confirm the theory? How?

7   The ferns could remove arsenic from soil polluted by industry. But what if beneficial insects took a bite from their leaves? And what if the plants spread throughout the countryside and turned into an invasive species?

Summing up

8   What is bioaccumulation?

9   Which three minerals do plants need most?

10   Describe the route water takes as it travels through a plant.

11   Explain why sunflowers can stand up straight without skeletons to support them.

12   Suggest a reason why a plant might store harmful chemicals in its leaves.

Get this

- Root hairs take up water and minerals, and stomata let water evaporate from leaves.
- Plants need nitrates, phosphates and potassium and minute amounts of other metals.

4.1 Diamonds are forever

Making diamonds

Diamonds are forever. But where do they come from and how were they made?

It is 500 million years ago. In the top part of the Earth's mantle, 170 km below the surface, is a tiny **carbon atom**. The temperature is about 1000 °C. Huge forces push on the atom, and on atoms nearby.

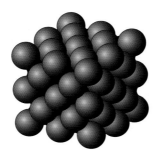

At this **temperature** and **pressure** our carbon atom joins strongly to other carbon atoms. The atoms arrange themselves in a pattern. Millions more carbon atoms join the pattern. A **crystal** forms.

 1 Is the crystal an **element** or a **compound**? Explain how you decided.

The pattern of atoms in the crystal makes it a particularly rare and beautiful type of carbon, diamond.

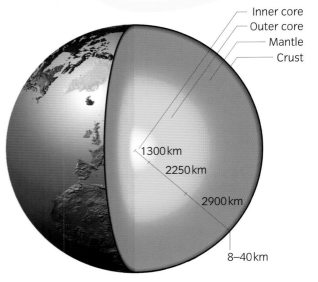

Inner core
Outer core
Mantle
Crust

1300 km
2250 km
2900 km
8–40 km

▶ Diamond encrusted skull by Damian Hirst

On the move

The diamond stays where it is, surrounded by solid rock, for 440 million years. One day, movements from deep in the Earth start pushing liquid rock upwards. As the **magma** forces its way up, it rips off small pieces of solid rock. Inside one of these pieces is our diamond.

The magma carries our diamond up with it. By the time it gets to the surface, it is moving very fast.

The magma breaks through the rocks of the Earth's surface. Then whoosh! It zooms high into the sky. With it goes the rock that contains our diamond.

The liquid (now called **lava**) falls to the ground. It solidifies. Our diamond is hidden inside.

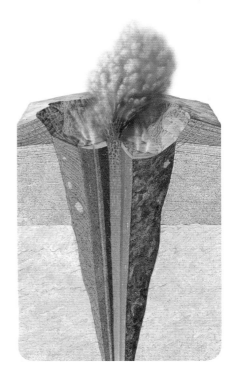

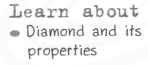

Learn about
● Diamond and its properties

2 The liquid rock starts off in the mantle. What is the scientific name for the part of the Earth it travels through next?

3 What do scientists call liquid rock when it is below the Earth's surface? What do they call it above the surface?

Thousands of years later, rivers and streams begin flowing. One stream flows over the rock that hides our diamond. The rock starts to move with the water.

Many years later, all the rock around the diamond has broken off. Our diamond is exposed amongst the **sediment** at the bottom of the stream.

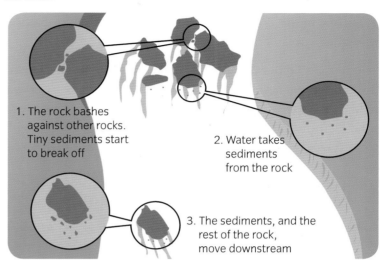

1. The rock bashes against other rocks. Tiny sediments start to break off

2. Water takes sediments from the rock

3. The sediments, and the rest of the rock, move downstream

 4 Match each of these scientific terms to one of the processes 1–3 in the diagram above: transportation, weathering, erosion.

Found!

It is now 1770. In Brazil, a man searches for diamonds. Carefully, he washes sand and gravel from the bottom of a stream. Suddenly, he spots our diamond.

It is undamaged. Diamond is hard, so it is not broken down by weathering. It is insoluble, so it has not dissolved in the stream.

The man sells the diamond, along with many others.

The diamonds are cut and polished. Rich people buy most of them for jewellery.

But the future of our diamond will be different.

▲ Raw diamonds

Summing up

5 In which part of the Earth is diamond formed?

6 Diamond is one form of the element carbon. What makes it an element?

7 What properties make it possible to say that 'diamonds are forever'?

Get this
- Diamond forms deep in the Earth.
- It is made of carbon atoms.
- Diamond is very hard and insoluble.

Learn about
● Evidence and theory

Disappearing diamond

In Europe in the 1700s, chemists were curious about diamond. What were the secrets of its beauty?

Scientists in France and Italy heated diamonds in air. They repeated the experiment several times. Usually, the diamonds glowed bright red. Often, they then disappeared. The scientists concluded that the solid diamonds had become a gas, or **sublimed**. Subliming happens when a solid is heated and becomes a gas without melting first.

1 Why did the scientists repeat the experiment?

2 What is subliming? Is it a physical or chemical change?

To sublime or burn?

Another French scientist, Antoine Lavoisier, thought that the evidence that diamonds sublimed was weak. He wanted more evidence. So he heated diamonds in a sealed glass container. After three hours of violent heating, he weighed them. Their mass was less than at the start. Were the other scientists right, after all?

3 How did Lavoisier's evidence support the conclusion of the other scientists?

▲ Lavoisier's apparatus.

Lavoisier then heated a diamond without air. It did not change and neither did its mass. Lavoisier was surprised. It seemed that diamond needed air to disappear. Perhaps the diamond had not sublimed, but burned?

Lavoisier did many more experiments, often using a huge burning glass to focus heat from the Sun onto the diamonds. When heated in air, the diamonds disappeared. Afterwards, there was a gas in the container that turned limewater milky white.

4 What is the difference between subliming and burning?

5 Which gas makes limewater milky?

Lavoisier **concluded** that the theory that diamond sublimes is wrong. His evidence made him conclude that diamond burns. He was not certain what diamond was, but knew that it contained carbon.

6 What evidence showed that diamond burns?

7 What evidence showed that diamond contains carbon?

More burning evidence

In England, Smithson Tennant heard of Lavoisier's work, and investigated further. He burned equal masses of diamond and charcoal. They made equal masses of carbon dioxide gas. He said that this evidence showed that diamond is pure carbon, like charcoal.

8 What did Tennant find out that Lavoisier didn't know?

9 Write an equation for the burning reaction of carbon.

In 1814, Humphrey Davy heard about the work of Lavoisier and Tennant. Davy wanted to try to replicate their results. He and Michael Faraday bought our diamond. They heated it strongly with a burning glass. Faraday recorded his **observations**:

The heat …continued for 3/4 of an hour ... On a sudden Sir H Davy observed the diamond to burn visibly…. The diamond glowed brilliantly with a scarlet light, inclining to purple and, when placed in the dark, continued to burn for about four minutes.

10 What observations suggested there was a chemical reaction?

Davy had **predicted** just one product for the reaction, the compound carbon dioxide. His prediction was correct. The evidence added further support to Tennant's theory that diamond is a form of pure carbon.

11 At the end of the experiment, where was our carbon atom? What atoms was it joined to?

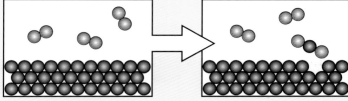

Key: ⊙⊙ An oxygen molecule
⊙⊙⊙ A carbon dioxide molecule
⬡ Diamond

▲ The particles in burning diamond.

Other forms of carbon

Not all solid carbon is diamond. Different atom arrangements give different forms of the element. Diamond is the hardest natural substance, so it is used for cutting and in drill tips.

▲ Graphite is pure carbon. It is soft, so it makes good pencils.

▲ Barbeque charcoal is almost pure carbon.

Summing up

12 What investigation could you do to check that graphite is pure carbon?

Get this

• Evidence can support or disprove scientific theories.

Into the air

150 million years ago, another carbon atom is expelled in the dying breath of a diplodocus.

The carbon atom is not on its own. It is strongly joined to two oxygen atoms. The three atoms together make up a **molecule** of the compound carbon dioxide. Its formula is CO_2.

 1 Our carbon dioxide molecule is the same as every other carbon dioxide molecule. How many carbon and oxygen atoms are in one carbon dioxide molecule?

2 Grace builds a model carbon dioxide molecule (below). Kate represents it with a formula, CO_2. How is Grace's representation better? What are the advantages of writing a formula?

Our molecule swoops around in the atmosphere, along with billions of others. Some of the other molecules are of carbon dioxide. Many more are molecules of elements, such as oxygen and nitrogen.

The atmosphere also contains argon. Argon atoms do not join to other atoms to make molecules. They exist as single atoms. The formula of argon gas is Ar.

 3 The atmosphere is a mixture of gases. Name one compound and three elements in the mixture.

4 An oxygen molecule consists of two oxygen atoms, strongly joined together. Its formula is O_2. A nitrogen molecule consists of two nitrogen atoms. What is its formula?

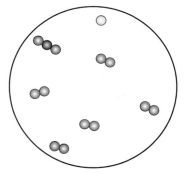

Key:
    A nitrogen molecule
    An oxygen molecule
    A carbon dioxide molecule
    An argon atom

▲ Particles in the air.

Captured!

Ten years later, our carbon atom is still tightly joined to two oxygen atoms in its carbon dioxide molecule. Suddenly, the molecule brushes against a wave in the sea. It mixes with the water, and dissolves. The molecule has not changed. But it is no longer part of the air. It is part of the mixture that makes up the sea.

For a few days, the carbon dioxide molecule moves around in the sea. One day, it meets a tiny floating plant and gets into it through a tiny hole. Inside the plant, something amazing happens.

Back to a body

The molecule enters a plant cell. Here, it meets more molecules, of water and carbon dioxide. The chloroplasts in the cell use energy from sunlight to make the water and carbon dioxide react together.

The atoms rearrange themselves and make new molecules, of glucose and oxygen. Our carbon atom hasn't disappeared – it can't! It is part of a new glucose molecule. The glucose molecule stays in the tiny plant, at least for now. The reaction is called photosynthesis.

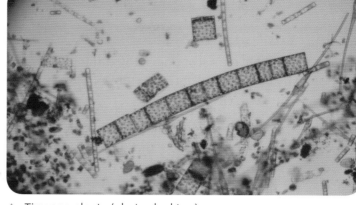
▲ Tiny sea plants (phytoplankton)

5 The word equation for photosynthesis is:
carbon dioxide + water → glucose + oxygen
Name the products of the reaction.

6 A glucose molecule consists of atoms of carbon, hydrogen and oxygen. Is it an element or compound? Explain how you decided.

7 The formula of glucose is $C_6H_{12}O_6$. Give the numbers of each type of atom in a glucose molecule.

The tiny floating plant does not survive long. A tiny sea animal comes along. It eats the plant. Our carbon atom is now part of its body.

An hour later, the tiny sea animal dies. It falls to the bottom of the sea, taking our carbon atom with it. What will happen to it next?

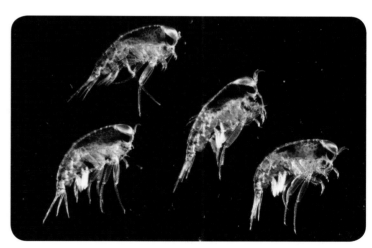
▲ Tiny sea animals (zooplankton)

Get this

- Compounds consist of atoms of two or more elements, strongly joined together.
- The air is a mixture of gases.
- In photosynthesis, carbon dioxide and water make glucose and oxygen.

Summing up

8 Give the names and formulae of two compounds. What makes them compounds?

9 Name the reactants and products of photosynthesis.

Learn about
- Oil and methane formation
- Burning hydrocarbons

Making methane

We left our carbon atom just under 150 million years ago, in the body of a tiny dead animal at the bottom of the sea. Millions of other dead sea creatures collect here.

Layers of sand and mud quickly bury the bodies. Over millions of years, the layers form rock above the bodies. As more layers form, the downwards pressure increases. So does the temperature. The bodies of the tiny sea animals slowly decay.

Our carbon atom takes part in just one of the many millions of decay reactions that happen over the next 100 million years. Decay reactions often involve oxygen. But there is no oxygen beneath the rocks. So our carbon atom joins to four hydrogen atoms to make a molecule of a new compound – methane. Many other methane molecules form, too.

▲ Shells on the seafloor

1 Name the two elements in methane.

2 The formula of methane is CH_4. How many atoms of carbon and hydrogen are in one methane molecule?

3 Methane is a gas at room temperature. Describe the movement and arrangement of its molecules.

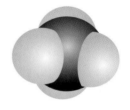

▲ A methane molecule CH_4

More hydrocarbons

Other compounds form at the same time as methane. The molecules of most of these compounds consist of chains of carbon atoms joined to hydrogen atoms. The compounds are **hydrocarbons**. The mixture of hydrocarbons is crude oil. One of the hydrocarbons is octane, which is used in petrol. Its formula is C_8H_{18}, so its molecules have 8 carbon atoms and 18 hydrogen atoms.

For 50 million years our carbon atom remains beneath the sea, locked in its methane molecule.

In 2001, an oil company drills a hole in the rocks under the North Sea. Our methane molecule moves upwards. It enters a pipeline, and moves towards land.

Burn!

After a long journey westwards, through narrower and narrower pipes, our methane molecule comes out of a tiny nozzle in a gas cooker. So do millions of other molecules. Someone lights the gas. There is a chemical reaction. The bonds that joined our carbon atom to four hydrogen atoms for 50 million years have been broken. Our atom is joined to two oxygen atoms in a molecule of carbon dioxide. Atoms have again been rearranged, this time in a combustion reaction.

 4 The word equation for the reaction is:

methane + oxygen → carbon dioxide + water

Name the **reactants**.

5 Give the **formulae** of carbon dioxide and water.

6 Hydrocarbons burn to make carbon dioxide and water. Write a word equation for burning octane.

Where is our carbon atom now? Well, the carbon dioxide molecule moves away from the cooker, out of an open window and into the air. It is there now – swooping round and bumping into other molecules.

We've followed our carbon atom on a long journey, lasting more than 150 million years. It has ended up back where it started.

 7 Draw an illustrated flow diagram to show the journey of our carbon atom.

Summing up

8 Oxygen is not involved in the decay of dead sea creatures under rocks. Why?

9 Give the names and formulae of two compounds that form when sea creatures decay under rocks over millions of years.

10 Why is oil **non-renewable**?

11 Heptane is a hydrocarbon. Name two products that form when it burns.

Get this

- Methane and oil form when dead sea creatures decay under rocks.
- This takes millions of years.
- When hydrocarbons burn, the products are carbon dioxide and water.

Learn about
- Making limestone and marble

Volcano to seashell

We join our third carbon atom 450 million years ago. It is thrown out of a volcano as part of a carbon dioxide molecule. The molecule moves around in the atmosphere.

The carbon dioxide molecule dissolves in a warm, shallow sea. It is surrounded by water molecules and particles of salts.

1 The sea is a solution. Name the solvent and one solute.

2 What atoms are in a carbon dioxide molecule?

In the sea, the carbon dioxide molecule reacts with a water molecule. One of the products is a **carbonate** particle. Our carbon atom is in the middle of this particle, strongly joined to three oxygen atoms.

A scallop takes the carbonate particle into its body. It uses calcium and carbonate particles to grow a hard shell to protect its soft body. Our carbon atom becomes part of the calcium carbonate which makes up this shell.

From shell to rock

The scallop dies, and falls to the bottom of the sea. Its body decays, but its shell stays on the seabed with millions of others. The shells break into small pieces, with water flowing between them. More shells fall on top. Their weight squashes together the small shell pieces below them, and squeezes out the water. The water leaves behind a mineral 'cement'. This joins the shell pieces together to form a rock – **limestone**.

Our carbon atom is now one of billions of tiny atoms in a layer of rock several metres thick and many metres wide. It is still holds tightly to three oxygen atoms in its carbonate particle.

 3 Why is limestone a **sedimentary** rock?

4 Limestone often contains fossils. Why?

5 How might you work out which parts of Britain were once covered by shallow seas?

Years later, very hot magma forces its way into the limestone from deep under the Earth. The intense heat makes the calcium and carbonate particles arrange themselves in a new pattern of bigger crystals which interlock tightly. A new rock – **marble** – is formed.

 6 Why is marble is a **metamorphic** rock?

7 Marble is mainly calcium carbonate, like limestone. Name the three elements in this compound.

Solid as a rock?

Nothing happens to the marble for millions of years. Then, about two thousand years ago, Roman workers dig up a lump of this beautiful rock. Our carbon atom is part of the lump. The workers cut the marble to make a counter top for a fast food restaurant in the city of Pompeii.

 8 What properties of marble means it makes good counter tops?

In the year 79 CE, Mount Vesuvius erupts. It buries Pompeii and its people in mud and ash. The counter top – and our carbon atom within it – is buried too.

In the 1700s, archaeologists uncover the counter top. It is exposed to the rain. Rain is acidic. Slowly, the marble reacts with the acid in the rain. One day, our carbon atom takes part in this reaction. The carbonate particle in which it has been locked for millions of years splits up. A carbon dioxide molecule forms, and escapes. Our carbon atom is part of the atmosphere again.

 9 Name one reactant and one product in the reaction of marble with acidic rain.

▲ A roman counter-top at Pompeii

Summing up

10 Describe how limestone forms. Use these words – seashell, sediment, squash, cement.

11 Describe what happens to the particles when limestone forms marble.

Get this

- Limestone forms from seashell sediments that are squashed and cemented together.
- Marble forms when limestone is changed by underground heat.

4.6 The carbon cycle

Learn about
- Carbon in living things
- The carbon cycle

Element of life

We left our carbon atoms in the air in carbon dioxide molecules. Their journeys will continue.

Plants use carbon dioxide in photosynthesis to make glucose and oxygen. The oxygen goes into the air. Most oxygen in the atmosphere has been released by plants.

In plants, some glucose molecules join together to make starch molecules, like those in potatoes. Others take part in reactions to make proteins, like those in beans. If an animal eats the plant, all the plant's compounds go into the animal.

Plants and animals use glucose for respiration. Respiration happens in every cell, when glucose and oxygen react to release energy. The products are carbon dioxide and water.

When plants and animals die, bacteria and fungi feed on them. The bacteria and fungi respire, making carbon dioxide. The cycle continues.

 1 Name the reactants in photosynthesis and respiration. The equations are:

Photosynthesis: carbon dioxide + water → glucose + oxygen

Respiration: glucose + oxygen → carbon dioxide + water

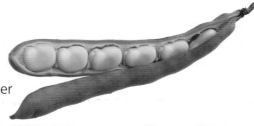

Modelling carbon's journey

All the time, carbon moves between living things and the environment as its compounds take part in chemical reactions. Scientists summarise these in a **model** called the **carbon cycle**.

The carbon cycle shows four main carbon stores:

- The deep ocean
- Fossil fuels
- Land-based plants and animals, and the soil
- The atmosphere

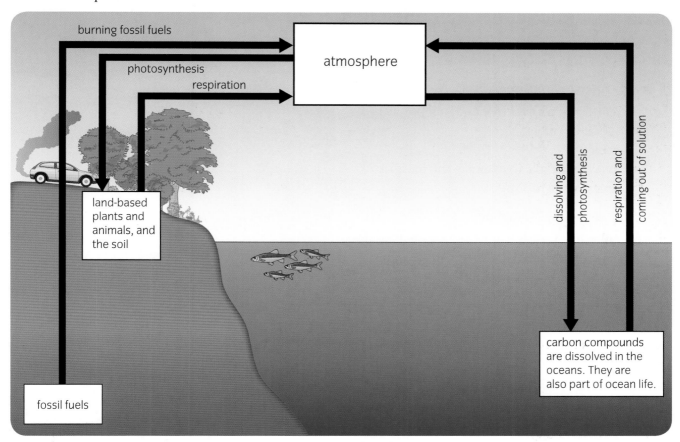

Get this

- Photosynthesis removes carbon dioxide from the atmosphere.
- Respiration releases carbon dioxide.
- The carbon cycle models carbon's journeys.

Summing up

2 Use the carbon cycle to describe three ways of adding carbon dioxide to the atmosphere.

3 How does carbon dioxide leave the atmosphere?

Storing carbon in plants

Trees matter

Plants, particularly trees, are a vital carbon store. How much carbon is locked within them? What is the impact on the carbon cycle of cutting down or burning trees?

? **1** Why is it important to discover how much carbon plants store?

Measuring the carbon stored in plants

How much carbon is stored by the plants of the Earth? This is a difficult question. Scientists use several methods to find an answer.

1. Destructive **sampling**:

    - cut down a forest tree and pull out its roots
    - dry it all out
    - weigh it
    - use the sample to estimate the mass of trees in the forest.

2. Non-destructive sampling:

    - measure a tree's height and trunk diameter
    - use this data to calculate its mass and estimate the mass of all the trees in the forest.

3. **Remote sensing**:

    - use satellite image data to estimate the area of a forest
    - on the ground, observe the types and ages of trees in the forest
    - do a calculation to estimate the mass of trees.

The scientists then use an equation to estimate the mass of carbon in the measured tree masses.

Remote sensing needs scientists from different specialisms. Space scientists design satellites and plan their orbits. Biologists classify trees on the ground. Physicists are researching new remote sensing methods. They plan to use light reflected by leaves to estimate the masses of trees from above.

? **2** Explain why each technique gives an estimate of carbon mass, not an accurate value.

3 You have lots of tiny bonsai trees. How would you estimate the amount of carbon stored in them?

Learn about

- Estimating carbon stored in plants
- Scientists collaborating

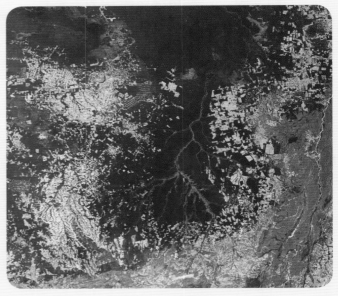

▲ Satellite image of a rainforest

4 How would you estimate the amount of carbon stored in five beech trees in the park?

5 How would you estimate the amount of carbon stored in a rainforest?

Working together

Millions of pounds are spent collecting data about the carbon cycle. Scientists need to share **data** and theories so that they learn from each other and do not waste their efforts. This is called **collaboration**.

In 1997, scientists in Brazil got together to do just this. They wanted to learn more about the impacts of felling and burning rainforest trees. They wrote a list of important questions. Over 600 scientists from all over the world are working in teams to answer the questions.

The teams design experiments and collect data. They share the data on a web site. Many of the teams have created posters to summarise their data and theories. They display and discuss these at conferences and workshops. The teams are now using the Internet to work together to pull out the most important lessons from their research.

▲ Logging a rainforest.

One team worked on a question about how logging affects the exchange of carbon dioxide between trees and the atmosphere. They compared the concentrations of carbon dioxide in the air in two areas of forest. Overall, more carbon dioxide entered the atmosphere in the area that was logged. The scientists suggested two reasons for this:

● Less photosynthesis happens in the logged area.
● There is more woody waste for fungi to decay in the logged area.

6 Describe some benefits of the Brazilian project.

7 Explain how less photosynthesis and more woody waste lead to more carbon dioxide in the atmosphere.

Summing up

8 Describe three methods of estimating the amounts of carbon stored in trees, and say when you would use each method.

9 Describe how the scientists on the Brazilian project collaborate.

Get this

● Scientists use sampling and remote sensing to estimate plant carbon stores.
● Scientists collaborate by sharing data and theories.

Carbon dioxide – climate culprit?

Learn about
- Evidence and cause

▲ Tree ring growth

Hotter and hotter?

Life depends on carbon dioxide in the atmosphere. Carbon dioxide traps heat from the Sun. Too little carbon dioxide, and Earth would be too cold for life. Too much, and Earth would be too hot.

Over the past 600 million years, the Earth has got colder and hotter several times. In cooler times, much of the Earth was covered in ice. In warmer times, Britain was beneath tropical seas. Scientists use evidence from tree rings, sea sediments and ice cores to estimate early Earth temperatures.

1 Why can scientists not have precise data about early Earth temperatures?

In 1998, three scientists published the 'hockey stick graph'. This showed that the Earth was warmer then than it had been for over 1000 years. Other scientists claimed the graph was incorrect. More data was collected. The extra data supported the original conclusion.

2 Why is it called the 'hockey stick graph'?

3 Why did scientists want more data?

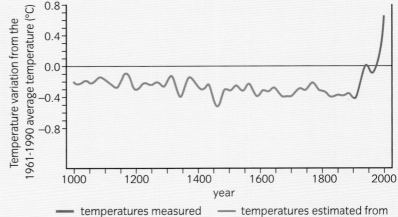

— temperatures measured with thermometers — temperatures estimated from tree rings and ice cores etc.

▲ Variation in temperatures 1000–2000 **CE**

Measuring carbon dioxide

Burning **fossil fuels** puts carbon dioxide into the atmosphere. Our use of fossil fuels increased rapidly in the twentieth century. In the 1950s, scientists began to wonder whether extra carbon dioxide might affect our climate. A group decided to measure the concentration of carbon dioxide in the atmosphere, and see how it changed in future.

The group set up an observatory on the slopes of a Hawaiian mountain. The site was perfect. It was far from cities. Another mountain shielded it from dust and wind.

4 Why was the observatory on a Hawaiian mountain, not in a big city?

Fifty years later, scientists in Hawaii still collect carbon dioxide data. They use an infrared carbon dioxide analyser to get accurate measurements.

▲ The observatory, Hawaii

Observatory director says: 'Carbon dioxide is…a very small part of the atmosphere, so we need to track it very accurately. Even small changes in carbon dioxide have a big effect on the atmosphere.'

5 Why is carbon dioxide measured all the time, not just once a week.

6 The graph summarises the Hawaii data. Describe the pattern.

7 The two graphs on this spread have similar shapes. Does this prove that carbon dioxide causes climate change?

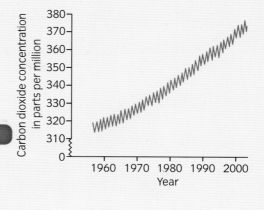

Carbon dioxide – climate culprit?

The two graphs show that the patterns of temperature and carbon dioxide increases are similar. But they cannot show whether one causes the other. Scientists collected more evidence. Much of this supports the theory that carbon dioxide causes climate change:

- Lab experiments – carbon dioxide absorbs infrared radiation (heat)
- Data analysis – for the past 500 000 million years, as carbon dioxide levels have gone up and down, so have temperatures. The two graph shapes are similar.

Some people argue with the theory. They say that natural events – like sunspots or changes in the Earth's orbit – are more important causes of climate change.

Answers and action

Does carbon dioxide cause climate change? What will the consequences be? Can we prevent climate crisis? Governments wanted answers. They set up the Intergovernmental Panel on Climate Change (IPCC), led by Indian scientist Rajendra Pachauri.

The IPCC studied evidence from 2500 scientists from over 100 countries. Their 2007 report concluded that global warming is definitely happening. Greenhouse gases from human activity are the 'very likely' cause. Climate change will probably cause sea level rises, heat waves and heavy rainfall.

The report convinced some governments of the need to take action to prevent climate change. Many plans are in place. But will action follow, and will it be effective? Time will tell...

Summing up

8 What evidence supports the theory that carbon dioxide causes climate change?

9 Why are the purposes of the IPCC?

10 How reliable are the report's conclusions? Why?

Get this

- Conclusions must be supported by evidence.

Learn about
- Scientists developing new products
- Particles and properties

How Science Works

Do you have favourite trainers, or a pair you desperately want? Sports shoes are not simply fashion items. They are designed to perform – to win records for their wearers and sales for their manufacturers.

Every sport has different shoe requirements. Companies like Nike, Reebok and Puma employ scientists to help meet these needs. Their lab teams may include **materials scientists**, sports scientists and **physiologists**.

1 Why do scientists of different disciplines work together to create sports shoes?

Light as a feather

If you run, jump or play basketball, you don't want to be held back by the weight on your feet. Sports shoe companies work hard to make lighter shoes.

Scientist Jay Meschter looked at sports shoe embroidery. He wondered if threads could be used for more than decoration. Maybe they could hold a shoe together, like wires in a suspension bridge.

Jay and his team created a 'Roman Sandal', in which straps attached a shoe sole to a runner's foot. As the athlete ran, scientists measured the forces on the straps. Foot parts where the forces were greatest would need the most threads, they reasoned.

The next challenge was to make the threads. Jay needed to find the best material for the job.

2 What properties must the thread material have?

Jay was inspired by carbon fibre, used for bikes and fishing rods. He admired its strength and lightness, but its stiffness and brittleness made it no good for shoes.

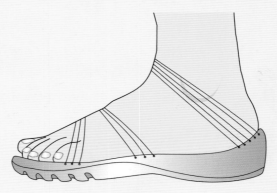

Jay experimented with Kevlar, used in bullet-proof vests. He persuaded the Kevlar company to supply extra thin threads. But the Kevlar damaged the shoemaking machinery. Time to think again.

Jay studied data on other materials. He found a very flexible material – Vectran. The table compares Vectran with other materials.

Material	Strength	Density
Carbon fibre	5.6	1.6
Kevlar	3.6	1.4
Vectran	3.0	1.4
Stainless steel	2.0	7.9

 3 What properties make Vectran the best material for sports shoe threads?

Vectran – the inside story

Vectran is a **polymer**. It consists of rings of carbon atoms, joined together in long chains. Vectran thread is flexible because its long molecules can slide past each other. It is strong because its chains line up in the same direction.

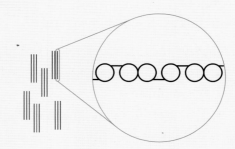

Jay used Vectran thread to make sports shoes. Athletes loved the shoes' lightness, and the way they moved with their skin. The company now uses the threads in basketball, tennis and running shoes.

 4 Explain why Vectran thread is flexible and strong.

Polymer protection

When you run, you exert a force of three times your weight on each foot, every step. The graph shows the forces on a foot during one step.

 5 In one step, which part of your foot feels a force first?

6 Where on your foot is the impact force more sudden?

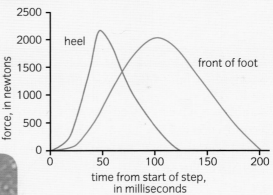

Impact forces cause injury, so sports shoe cushioning must reduce the forces. Many sports shoes contain EVA (ethyl vinyl acetate). EVA is made as a polymer foam, with thousands of tiny air-filled holes. Landing on your foot pushes out the air. When you take your foot off the ground, air returns to the holes, ready to cushion your next step.

EVA is flexible and has a low density, but it doesn't last long. Runners complain their shoes feel 'flat'. This is because the foam has compressed. The holes have got smaller, and hold less air than before.

Summing up

7 Outline the stages the scientists went through to develop the shoes.

Get this

- Data and creative thinking help scientists develop new products.

Learn about
- Using data to compare material properties
- The reactivity series

Record breaker

In 2007, British teenager Michael Perham stepped off his yacht *Cheeky Monkey* to a hero's welcome in Antigua. Michael had just set a new world record. At fourteen, he was the youngest person to sail single-handed across the Atlantic.

The hull of the yacht was made from glass reinforced plastic, GRP, or fibreglass. GRP consists of a plastic resin reinforced by thin glass strands as shown in the picture.

The two materials work together:
- The plastic resin withstands big squashing forces, but is weak when pulled.
- The glass fibres are strong when pulled, but weak when compressed.

Combining the two materials in GRP makes a material that withstands both squashing and stretching forces – vital when a thin boat hull is the only thing between you and the sea.

 1 Explain why it is better to build a boat from GRP than from plastic resin alone.

Metals versus fibreglass

Not all boats have **fibreglass** hulls. This boat is made from **metal**.

Metal boats have many advantages. First, they can be very strong. Second, metals stretch. So if a metal boat hits a rock, it may be dented but not holed. Fibreglass is brittle. It is more likely to be holed on collision.

 2 Give two properties of metals which mean they make good boats.

Metal decision

Aluminium alloys and **steel** are popular boatbuilding materials.

Property	Aluminium alloy 5083	ABS steel (an alloy of iron)
Density (g/cm^3)	2.65	7.1
Tensile strength (force to pull a material until it breaks) (MPa)	300	400 – 490
Yield strength (the maximum force a material can withstand before it changes shape permanently), in MPa	150	235

3 Which metal breaks more easily?

4 Which metal bends more and still springs back into shape?

5 You have two identical boats, one made of aluminium and the other of steel. Which is lighter?

6 Suggest two advantages of steel boats.

Enemy at sea

Boats face many dangers. One comes from seawater itself. Some metals react with water, or salts and oxygen dissolved in it. This is **corrosion**.

The **reactivity series** lists metals in order of reactivity. Metals at the top react most vigorously with water and oxygen.

 7 Predict which is damaged more by corrosion – aluminium or iron. Explain why.

Aluminium is above iron, so you might predict that it is damaged more by corrosion. But this is not the case. Freshly-cut aluminium quickly reacts with oxygen from the air. A thin, hard aluminium oxide coating forms. This stops water and oxygen molecules hitting the aluminium atoms below. The aluminium cannot react. It is protected from corrosion.

Steel corrodes more easily. Its iron atoms react with water and oxygen molecules to make hydrated iron oxide. This is reddish-brown rust, which flakes off. Holes may form – and let water in!

It is vital to protect steel hulls. Paint offers good protection, except when scratched. Many steel boats have a piece of zinc attached to them. Zinc is more reactive than iron. It reacts with water, salts and oxygen instead of iron. The zinc is sacrificed to save the iron, so this is called **sacrificial protection**.

 8 Write word equations for the formation of aluminium oxide and rust.

9 Suggest another metal to use for sacrificial protection.

The Reactivity Series
Potassium
Sodium
Calcium
Magnesium
Aluminium
Zinc
Iron
Lead
Copper
Silver
Gold

Summing up

10 Aluminium conducts heat better than steel. Why is this a problem for sailors?

11 Write a paragraph about the advantages and drawbacks of fibreglass, aluminium and steel boats.

Get this

- Data helps us make decisions about materials.
- Usually, the more reactive the metal, the faster it corrodes.

5.3 Cars

Learn about
- Using science to reduce car CO_2 emissions
- Using data to compare cars

Faster than a bullet

British engineers are designing the world's first 1000 mph car, Bloodhound SCC. They want the car to beat the existing land speed record by more than 250 mph. Former RAF fighter pilot Andy Green will drive the car. 'It's an opportunity to do something extraordinary in engineering terms,' he said. The engineers face huge challenges. Bloodhound's wheels will spin five times faster than Formula One car wheels, generating forces that could rip them to pieces. There must be no gaps around the cockpit. If there are, the air inside could be sucked out.

1 Why do engineers want to make a 1000 mph car?

2 Describe two challenges for the engineers.

Bloodhound fuel

The car will have an aeroplane jet engine and a rocket booster. Together, they will generate 200 000 N of thrust to push the car forward. The fuel for the jet engine is kerosene. Kerosene is a mixture of hydrocarbons. Hydrocarbons are compounds of just two elements, carbon and hydrogen. They burn to make two main products.

$$\text{kerosene} + \text{oxygen} \rightarrow \text{carbon dioxide} + \text{water}$$

The engineers estimate that Bloodhound will produce about 1000 kg of carbon dioxide for each full speed run.

3 Name the main products of the jet fuel **combustion** reaction.

Gas guzzler

Most normal cars burn hydrocarbons too, so producing carbon dioxide gas. Extra carbon dioxide in the atmosphere causes climate change. The European Union is forcing car makers to produce cars that emit less carbon dioxide.

Car makers have made a start. This 1959 Ford Anglia, used in a Harry Potter film, produced as much carbon dioxide per kilometre as 200 modern Ford Fiestas.

4 A modern Fiesta emits around 120 g of carbon dioxide per kilometre. Estimate the mass of carbon dioxide emitted by the old Ford Anglia.

Cars lose weight

The table shows the masses and carbon dioxide emissions of some Volkswagen cars.

Car model	Minimum car mass, in kg	Average CO_2 emissions in g/km
Fox	978	144
Polo	1000	138
New Golf	1142	149
Touran	1423	176
Toureg	2214	324

5 What relationship does the data show between car mass and CO_2 emissions?

6 Do you think that heavier cars cause increased CO_2 emissions? Why? How sure can you be?

Engineers have many ideas for making lighter cars. Most cars are made from steel, but this car is made of a lower-density aluminium alloy. Even simple things make a difference, such as having a puncture repair kit instead of a spare wheel.

Engines of the future

Most car engines burn a mixture of hydrocarbons. The energy from burning turns a shaft. The rotating shaft moves the vehicle. But car engines are inefficient. Only about 20% of the fuel's energy actually moves a car down the road. Most energy is wasted.

Car engines transfer much energy as heat. This is a waste. Honda engineers reduced the friction between the moving parts of the engine, so cutting down on waste heat and carbon dioxide.

Energy is also wasted by keeping the engine running in traffic jams and at red lights. So engineers designed a stop–start system to cut off the engine when the car stops, and start it when the driver presses the clutch.

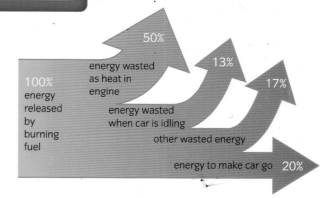

100% energy released by burning fuel

energy wasted as heat in engine — 50%

energy wasted when car is idling — 13%

other wasted energy — 17%

energy to make car go — 20%

Get this
- Engineers use science to reduce car CO_2 emissions.

Summing up

7 List two ways in which cars waste energy.

8 Explain three ways of reducing car carbon dioxide emissions.

Silent solution?

2008 was a tough year for car makers. With less money around, people stopped buying cars. From October to December, Ford lost £2 million every hour. In January 2009, the usually buzzing Detroit car show was quiet. Some companies didn't bother turning up. Only cars offering a greener driving future seemed to do well.

Turn the key. Press the accelerator. And off you go – fast! No noise. No exhaust. No carbon dioxide. The car is fun to drive and cheap to run. BMW's battery-powered Mini E sounds too good to be true, and maybe it is. The company wants five hundred people to test drive the car for a year to help find out.

Huge, heavy batteries supply electricity to make the car go. But they don't last long. Every 150 miles, you must plug the car into the mains for a recharge – not convenient on long journeys!

And just how green are electric cars? It depends where the recharging electricity comes from.

1 Burning fossil fuels generate most UK electricity. Do electric cars really result in zero carbon dioxide emissions? Explain why.

Scientist Sebastien Ruiz works for an electricity company. He is optimistic about electric cars. Even generating electricity as we do now, he says, an electric car results in 40% smaller carbon dioxide emissions than a new petrol car.

2 Do you trust this scientist's opinion? Why?

3 Suggest a disadvantage of cars moving quietly.

The best of both worlds?

The Toyota Prius is a **hybrid car**. It has a small petrol engine which charges a battery. The battery powers an electric motor. At slow speeds, the motor moves the car. At faster speeds, the petrol engine cuts in.

4 Give an advantage of hybrid cars compared to electric cars.

5 Give an advantage of hybrid cars compared to petrol cars.

Hydrogen future?

The first hydrogen powered vehicle was made in 1908. It had one exhaust product – water. But hydrogen vehicles were not popular. People preferred petrol. Liquid petrol is easier to transport and store than hydrogen gas.

6 Write a word equation for the combustion reaction of hydrogen.

7 Give some advantages and disadvantages of hydrogen fuel.

Today, there is more interest in hydrogen cars. Some burn hydrogen in their engines, like Arnold Schwarzenegger's Hydrogen Hummer. But there won't be many of these – it needs refuelling every 60 miles.

The Honda FC sport has a hydrogen fuel cell. The fuel cell makes electricity. Hydrogen gas flows into the cell. There, it reacts with oxygen. The process generates electricity to move the car. There is one exhaust gas – water vapour.

8 Name the product made in a hydrogen fuel cell.

9 Describe the main difference between the two types of hydrogen car.

. The biggest question about hydrogen gas is where to get it from. There is no hydrogen gas on Earth. So hydrogen fuel must be manufactured. You can make hydrogen by reacting methane, from natural gas, with water. The reaction is:

methane + water → hydrogen + carbon monoxide

10 Carbon monoxide is poisonous, so it is reacted with oxygen as it is made. What is the product of this second reaction? What problems can this gas cause?

11 Companies might also make hydrogen gas by splitting up water with electricity. Is this a greener way of making hydrogen? Explain why.

▲ The Honda FC Sport

Summing up

12 Create a table showing the advantages and disadvantages of electric, hybrid and hydrogen fuel cell cars.

> ## Get this
> - Electric, hybrid and hydrogen fuel cell cars have advantages and disadvantages.

Train versus car

Callum, do you like my new car? It's one of the greenest around – it makes only 99 g of carbon dioxide per kilometre. So no need to worry about the environment now!

But Mum, that's 99 g too much. Why don't you walk for short journeys? And for long trips, it's much better to take the train.

Learn about
- Using secondary data to make travel decisions
- The benefits and drawbacks of new train fuels

Is Callum right? Is the train the greener option?

Shades of green

The table gives data on fuel use and carbon dioxide emission for cars and trains.

 1 Callum and his mum plan to drive 200 km in the Ford Fiesta to see relatives. How much fuel will they use? How much carbon dioxide will the car emit?

2 Explain why your answers to question 1 cannot be exact.

3 Callum's dad wants to join them the next day. Should he travel the 200 km in his Ford S-Max car, or by train? Use data to explain why.

Vehicle	Average fuel consumption, in litres / 100 km	Average CO$_2$ emissions, in g/km
Voyager diesel train	2.8 per passenger	74 per passenger
Ford Fiesta 1.6 TDCi Econetic car	4.2 per car	99 per car
Ford S-Max 2.0 Edge car	8.1 per car	194 per car

Greener trains

Train companies want to make train travel greener. British scientists made detailed measurements of train energy use. They calculated that switching off electric trains overnight and running shorter trains when there are fewer passengers could save 6% of the energy used to move trains.

In June 2008, when fuel prices hit record highs, train drivers saved fuel by driving smoothly instead of accelerating and braking sharply, and by coasting downhill.

4 Suggest why shorter trains save fuel.

Chip train

If you eat chips in Disneyland, you don't only refuel yourself. You also help fuel Disneyland's trains. The trains run on fuel made from used cooking oil from the resort's restaurants.

Cooking oil is a mixture of molecules made up of hydrogen, carbon and oxygen atoms. The atoms are joined together in chains. The fuel burns to make two main products: water and carbon dioxide.

The products when you burn petrol and diesel are the same. Petrol and diesel are also mixtures of molecules. The molecules consist of atoms of hydrogen and carbon. Petrol and diesel are separated from crude oil, formed from animals that lived millions of years ago. Cooking oil comes from plants that lived recently. As the plants grew, they took carbon dioxide from the atmosphere. Burning oil from the plants returns similar amounts of carbon dioxide to the atmosphere.

 5 Describe some benefits and problems of using cooking oil as a train fuel.

▲ Like Disneyland's trains this shuttle bus runs on biodiesel made from vegetable oil.

Cow power

Swedish scientists discovered another way of making train fuel – from dead cows. They take waste organs and fat from an abattoir that kills cows for food. Microbes digest the waste. This makes methane gas. Methane is a hydrocarbon. It burns to make carbon dioxide and water. Passengers went on Sweden's first biogas-powered train in 2005.

 6 Write an equation for burning methane.

7 What are the benefits of using cow waste methane instead of methane from natural gas?

Summing up

8 Describe the differences and similarities between cooking oil and petrol.

9 What fuels would you like future trains to use? Why?

Get this
- Emissions and fuel data help make travel decisions.
- Waste can be used to make train fuels.

Learn about
- Using primary and secondary data
- Making diesel

Bus benefits

Buses have environmental benefits. If all the passengers in a full bus went by car they would create far more carbon dioxide emissions. But there are drawbacks. Most buses burn diesel. This can damage health.

Burning diesel makes **particulate**s, as well as carbon dioxide and water. Particulates are tiny sooty particles, with diameters of about 0.0001 mm. They penetrate deep into the lungs.

Investigating particulates

Californian scientists investigated the health risks of diesel exhaust fumes inside school buses. They compared the exhaust inside school buses with the exhaust inside cars driving in front of the buses.

The scientists collected primary data. They:

- rented school buses;
- drove them along a school bus route;
- repeated the journey four more times;
- measured the amounts of particulates in the buses – at the back and front, and with open and shut windows;
- recorded their results;
- measured particulate amounts inside the car in front.

The scientists analysed their results. Exhaust levels varied hugely from bus to bus. Usually, particulate levels were higher at the back, and with closed windows. On average, the level at the back of a bus was four times the level of exhaust at the front.

The scientists studied data, collected by others, which estimates the risk of cancer when people are exposed to different amounts of diesel exhaust. They used this data, and their own, to calculate that a student using a Californian school bus regularly has up to 46 times the cancer risk defined as 'acceptable' by the US government.

1 Why did the scientists compare diesel levels in buses with those in cars?

2 Why did they repeat the journeys?

3 Identify the secondary data the scientists used.

Better buses

Many places are cleaning up their act by using diesel alternatives. Initiatives include:

- Using biodiesel. Biodiesel, made from plants, does not produce particulates. One company gives cheap tickets to people who donate used cooking oil to fuel its buses.
- Using hydrogen fuel cell buses.

Inside diesel

Diesel is a mixture of hydrocarbon compounds. Their molecules consist of hydrogen and carbon atoms. The formulae of its molecules range from $C_{10}H_{20}$ to $C_{15}H_{28}$.

Petrol is also a mixture of hydrocarbons, but its molecules are smaller. Most petrol molecules contain eight carbon atoms.

Diesel and petrol are made from **crude oil**. Crude oil is a **mixture** of hundreds of hydrocarbons. It is heated to over 450 °C so that most of its compounds become gases. The gases move up through a column, getting cooler all the time.

As the gases cool, they **condense**. Because they have different boiling points, they condense at different temperatures. Diesel compounds have high boiling points. They do not need to cool much to turn back into liquids. So they condense near the bottom of the column, where the temperature is around 250 °C. The liquid is drained off.

Higher up, between 25 °C and 75 °C, petrol compounds condense.

The process is called **fractional distillation**. It separates different **fractions** of crude oil.

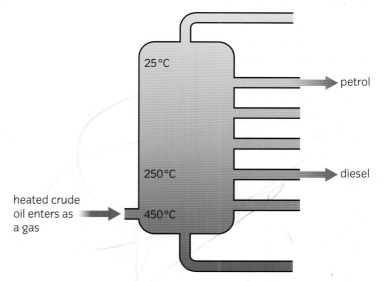

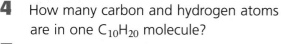 **4** How many carbon and hydrogen atoms are in one $C_{10}H_{20}$ molecule?

5 Why are petrol compounds collected higher up the column than diesel?

Summing up

6 How can particulates damage your health?

7 What primary data did the Californian scientists use?

8 What bus fuel would you recommend for school buses? Why?

Get this

- Scientists collect and analyse data to estimate health risks.
- Fractional distillation makes diesel from crude oil.

Killer noise?

The skies are getting busier. Every year, more aeroplanes take off from European airports. Nearby residents are concerned about their health. Are they right to worry?

▲ Local person

> Night landings disturb my sleep.

> There's no problem. Modern aircraft are quieter than ever.

▲ Airline employee

▲ European official

> Should we ban night flights? We need to know more.

The European Commission paid scientists from six countries to study aircraft noise and health. They designed an investigation to answer the question:

Does night-time aircraft noise increase the risk of high blood pressure?

People with high blood pressure are at risk of heart attacks and strokes.

Collecting data

The scientists obtained **secondary data** about noise levels (measured in **decibels**) near airports in six countries. They used this data to decide the study areas. They asked 6000 people from areas with different noise levels to join the study; 4861 agreed.

Next, the scientists collected **primary data**. They wanted their data to be:

● **Accurate** – as close as possible to correct values.
● **Reliable** – repeating the study gives data suggesting the same conclusions. Big samples give more reliable data.

They used automatic instruments to take three blood pressure measurements from each person. They asked questions about things that affect blood pressure, such as exercise and alcohol use.

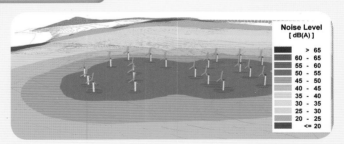

Noise Level
[dB(A)]

> 65
60 - 65
55 - 60
50 - 55
45 - 50
40 - 45
35 - 40
30 - 35
25 - 30
20 - 25
<= 20

▲ This is an example of a 3D sound/ noise contour map – it is for the construction of a small wind turbine farm

1 Why do you think the scientists did not collect their own noise level data?

2 Why did they use automatic blood pressure instruments?

3 Why did they take three measurements from each person, then calculate an average?

4 Why did the scientists recruit a large number of volunteers?

5 Suggest why the scientists asked about other factors affecting blood pressure.

Analysing data

The scientists put the data into a computer. They programmed the computer to do calculations on the data. It produced a graph:

The graph shows that for every 10 decibel increase in night-time aircraft noise, the risk of developing high blood pressure increases by about 14 %.

6 Copy and complete: A 75 decibel noise is twice as loud as a ___ decibel noise.

7 How much higher is the risk of developing high blood pressure in a 60 decibel area, compared to the quietest area?

8 How might the results influence the European official's view?

9 Would you trust the results more or less if an anti-airport group paid for the study? Why?

Bedroom research

The scientists wanted to examine their question more closely. They recruited 140 volunteers living near airports in four countries.

Nurses visited each volunteer. They set up a noise meter in the bedroom to record noise levels, and an MP3 recorder to identify noise sources later. Overnight, each person wore a blood pressure monitor. This recorded readings every 15 minutes.

The scientists analysed the results. Blood pressure levels increased when there were noises louder than 35 decibels in the 15 minutes before measurement. The results were similar for each country. This strengthens the evidence for the conclusion that noise *caused* the blood pressure increase.

The scientists suggested improvements for future work. They want blood pressure monitors that take measurements all the time and that do not disturb sleep.

Get this

- Accurate measurements are close to correct values.
- A reliable study is one which suggests similar results when repeated.

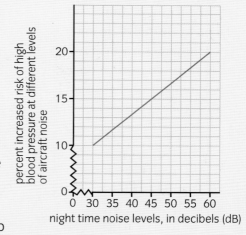

night time noise levels, in decibels (dB)

(y-axis: percent increased risk of high blood pressure at different levels of aircraft noise)

Summing up

10 Name three instruments that collected primary data.

11 How would improving blood pressure monitors increase accuracy?

12 Suggest a way of making this study more reliable.

13 How the scientists make sure the data in the first study were *accurate*?

14 How did the scientists make sure the first study was *reliable*?

15 Why did the second study strengthen evidence for aircraft noise *causing* high blood pressure?

Silent skies?

The challenge

Many people agree that aircraft noise is a problem. A group of British and American scientists and engineers decided to start from scratch to design a quiet aircraft. The Silent Airliner Initiative (SAI) was born.

Professor Ann Dowling, who led the British side of the project, recruited university scientists from Britain and the US; **engineers** from aircraft manufacturers; airline operators; measurement specialists and many other experts.

? **1** Why do you think Professor Dowling asked people with different skills and interests to join her?

Collaboration

Early on, the team realised that low noise could not be achieved by just one design feature. They needed many new features to create a quiet plane. Individuals and small groups worked on different design features. Scientists collaborated with aircraft industry engineers.

The teams needed to exchange information about ideas, experiments and results, and make decisions about what to do next. So they **communicated** by meeting every eight months, holding weekly video conferences, and e-mailing and phoning daily.

The teamwork was very successful – Professor Dowling says that in the SAI project, the whole result is greater than the sum of the separate parts.

? **2** What do you think Professor Dowling meant by this?
3 Why do you think the SAI collaboration worked well?

Quiet as a whisper?

The first thing you notice about the SAX-40 Silent Aircraft is its shape. Like Stealth Bombers, it has a blended wing design, with an all-in-one body and wings.

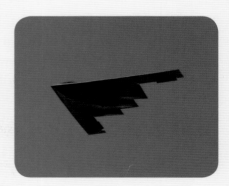

▲ A stealth bomber

In normal aircraft, only the wings provide lift. But in blended wing aircraft both the body and wings provide lift. With more lift the plane does not need to go as fast to lift off. It can also slow down more before landing. So the SAX-40 takes off and lands at slower speeds. This reduces the noise of air rushing over the body.

The picture shows some other design features of the SAX-40.

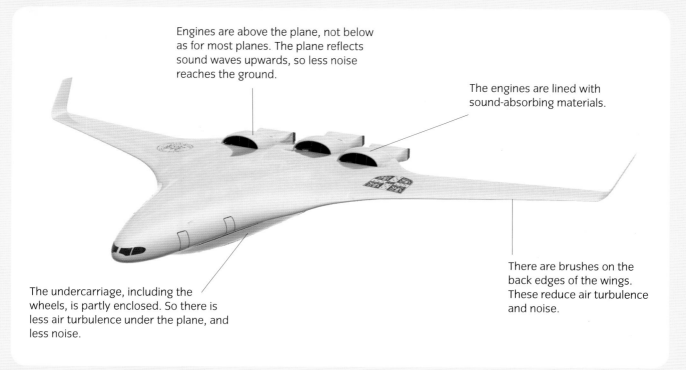

Engines are above the plane, not below as for most planes. The plane reflects sound waves upwards, so less noise reaches the ground.

The engines are lined with sound-absorbing materials.

The undercarriage, including the wheels, is partly enclosed. So there is less air turbulence under the plane, and less noise.

There are brushes on the back edges of the wings. These reduce air turbulence and noise.

 4 Describe five design features of the SAX-40. Explain how each helps to make the plane quiet.

Engineers predict that, at take off, the sound level would be 63 decibels. This is about the same as a busy street.

What next?

So far, the scientists have made only models of the SAX-40 and its components. It'll be a while before you see one in the skies! There are many challenges to overcome before a full size airliner can be made. One problem is finding a material to make the oval-shaped hull and blended wings. A very strong composite material must be developed, since the scientists have not found a metal or alloy with the necessary properties.

Summing up

5 The SAI project is hugely expensive – why might governments and companies want to fund it?

Get this

● Scientists collaborate with others from different disciplines because they have different skills and areas of expertise.

6.1 Can conundrum

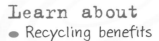

Learn about
- Recycling benefits

Can Man

It's 3 am. A police officer walks the streets of a crime hotspot. An elderly man is pushing a loaded shopping trolley. 'Odd time to be shopping,' thinks the officer. 'Is he a burglar? Better stop him.'

The man explains. His trolley contains aluminium drinks cans. He has collected them – ready squashed – from local pubs. Later, he will sell them to a recycling yard.

New from old

A recycling factory shreds the cans and removes their decoration. Then a massive furnace melts the aluminium shreds. The liquid aluminium is poured into a mould and cooled. The aluminium solidifies to make a 27 tonne ingot – equivalent to 27 small cars.

Use the data in the table below to answer the questions.

Aluminium data	Boiling point in °C	Melting point in °C
	2470	660

 1 Name the change of state when solid aluminium becomes liquid.

2 What is the lowest possible temperature for the furnace? Why?

Next, the ingot is heated to 600 °C to make it more bendy, and rolled into thin sheets. The sheets make around 1.5 million new cans. Six weeks after Can Man met the police, his aluminium is for sale again, in shiny new cans holding new fizzy drinks.

 3 What would happen if, before rolling, the ingot was heated to 700 °C instead of 600 °C?

From the Earth

All aluminium comes originally from the Earth's crust. But you can't just dig aluminium from the soil. Its atoms are strongly joined to atoms of other elements in compounds. Extracting aluminium involves breaking down one of these compounds – aluminium oxide.

Aluminium oxide is mixed with other substances in its ore, bauxite rock. Getting aluminium from bauxite involves
- crushing the ore and removing impurities
- dissolving the pure aluminium oxide in a special solvent.

- Passing a 100 000 amp electric current through the solution. The electricity splits up aluminium oxide to give liquid aluminium and other products.

 4 Many aluminium plants are near hydroelectric power plants. Suggest why.

Reasons to recycle

> Cans that are not recycled go to landfill. The more a local council dumps, the more it has to pay.

> Making recycled aluminium cans creates much less carbon dioxide than making cans from non-recycled aluminium.

> In early 2009, recycling companies paid £400 for a tonne of old cans.

> The world's aluminium ore will not last for ever.

> Producing 1 tonne of aluminium from its ore generates 3 tonnes of 'red mud' waste. Nothing grows on red mud. It may harm health.

 5 For each person listed below, choose one reason for recycling that they might think is important: someone living near an aluminium mine; a UK council official; Can Man; a climate change campaigner; a person with five great-grandchildren.

Energy savings

The table gives estimates of the energy for making aluminium in two ways.

| Energy to make 1 kg of aluminium, in MJ | |
...from recycled aluminium	...from bauxite ore
15	260

 6 Li uses 67 aluminium cans a year. Each can has a mass of 14.9 g. Show how to work out that the total mass of aluminium in his cans is about 1 kg.

7 Li recycles all 67 cans. Ben also uses 67 cans, but recycles none of them. How much energy does Li 'save' each year, compared to Ben?

8 It takes 2.45 MJ of energy to generate enough electricity to power Li's TV for one hour. For how long would the amount of energy Li 'saved' power his TV?

Summing up

9 Draw separate flow diagrams to show how aluminium cans are made from recycled aluminium and from aluminium ore.

Get this

- Recycling aluminium reduces energy use, toxic waste and carbon dioxide emissions.

Learn about
- Obtaining iron
- Fizzy drink solutions

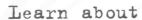

Steel recycling

Ella's can, like a quarter of all drinks cans, is made from steel. It contains 25% recycled steel.

At the recycling centre, huge magnets separate steel cans from aluminium ones. Steel is attracted to the magnets. Aluminium is not. The steel cans, and other steel waste, are crushed, tied into bales and taken to a steel plant for recycling.

 1 Ella tests a can with a magnet. The can is not attracted to it. Can Ella be sure the can is aluminium? Why?

Steel from rock

Steel is mainly iron. There is lots of **iron** in the Earth's crust. But the iron exists in compounds. The compounds must be broken down to get iron out of them.

Most common iron ores contain iron oxides. The oxides are heated with carbon. Carbon is more reactive than iron. It takes oxygen away from iron oxide:

iron oxide + carbon → iron + carbon dioxide

 2 Name the reactants and products in the reaction.

3 Which product is an unwanted waste substance?

4 The reaction happens in a furnace at about 2000 °C. Use the data to work out the state of iron at this temperature.
Data: melting point of iron = 1535 °C; boiling point of iron = 3000 °C.

Iron is lower in the reactivity series than aluminium. So it is joined less tightly to oxygen than aluminium is. That's why a simple chemical reaction extracts iron from its oxide, but a huge electric current is needed to obtain aluminium from its oxide.

Inside the can

Ella buys a can of 'Irn Bru'. The table shows some of its ingredients.

Ingredient (listed in April 2009)	Formula
Water	H_2O
Carbon dioxide	CO_2
Sugar (sucrose)	
Citric acid	$C_6H_8O_7$
Flavourings, including caffeine	$C_8H_{10}N_4O_2$
Preservative, E211 (sodium benzoate)	$C_7H_5O_2Na$

All the substances are compounds. They consist of atoms of two or more elements, held tightly together. Citric acid contains atoms of three elements – carbon, hydrogen and oxygen. The formula shows that in one citric acid molecule there are six carbon atoms, eight hydrogen atoms and seven oxygen atoms.

5 How does the formula of water show that it is a compound?

6 What is the total number of atoms in one citric acid molecule?

7 Name the elements that make up the compound sodium benzoate.

8 A sugar molecule consists of 12 carbon atoms, 22 hydrogen atoms and 11 oxygen atoms. Write its formula.

Canned drinks are **solutions**. In Irn Bru, water is the **solvent**. The other substances are **solutes**. The drink is made by **dissolving** the solutes in the solvent.

9 Copy the diagram of the solvent particles in a can of Irn Bru. Add circles of different colours to represent molecules of the solutes. Label your diagram.

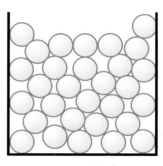

▲ Water particles in Irn Bru

Fizzy fun

It's summer, and Joe has been carrying a can of fizzy drink around in his bag all day. When he opens it – whoosh! The drink sprays everywhere. Why?

Carbon dioxide gas makes drinks fizzy. The gas is dissolved in the solvent. At high temperatures, less carbon dioxide can dissolve in the water. So when drinks warm up, carbon dioxide comes out of solution. In the can, it fills the space above the solution. The more gas in the space, the greater the pressure – and the faster the drink sprays out.

Summing up

10 Describe how iron is extracted from iron ore.

11 Name one compound in all fizzy drinks, and write its formula. How many atoms of each element are in one of its molecules?

Get this

- Heating iron ore with carbon makes iron.
- Water is the solvent in fizzy drinks.
- Carbon dioxide makes drinks fizzy.

Learn about
- Minerals in water

Bogus water

For months, office workers enjoyed Blenheim Palace mineral water from their water coolers. Then they started complaining that the water tasted funny. Scientists analysed water from the coolers. The amounts of the minerals dissolved in it were different from those of genuine Blenheim water. They suspected that the man paid by Blenheim Palace to bottle their mineral water had filled the bottles with tap water instead.

1 The scientists tested genuine Blenheim water and water cooler water. Which other water did they need to test before making their conclusion?

Mineral fingerprint

Mineral water comes from natural underground sources. Companies collect it from springs or boreholes. They may then **filter** the water before pouring it into bottles. Mineral water is not normally treated in any other way, so it must not contain harmful microbes.

2 What is the purpose of filtering mineral water?

Companies claim that every brand of mineral water tastes different. This is because each type flows through the pores of different types of rocks on its journey to the surface. On the way, it dissolves a unique combination of minerals. This gives the water its taste.

BUXTON

Water story 1

Rain falls in the Peak district. It soaks through the soil and travels through the pores of the limestone rock below, dissolving minerals during its journey. Five thousand years later the water bubbles out of a spring in Buxton like this one in St Ann's well.

PENNINE SPRING

Water story 2 – Pennine Spring

It's the 1950s. Rain falls over the Pennines. It soaks through the soil to the sandstone rock below. Fifty years later the water, rich in dissolved minerals, emerges at a spring.

3 How do minerals get into mineral water?

4 Which water spends longer underground – Buxton or Pennine Spring?

5 Give two possible reasons for this water spending longer underground.

Look at the label

Company scientists measure the amounts of minerals dissolved in their water. Bottles are labelled with the results.

The table gives data about some of the minerals in four mineral water brands.

Substance	\multicolumn{4}{c}{Amount of substance dissolved in 1 litre of mineral water, in mg}
	Volvic	Buxton	Pennine Spring	Brecon Carreg
Calcium	11.5	55	68	47.5
Magnesium	8.0	19	24	16.5
Sodium	11.6	24	30	5.7
Potassium	6.2	1	5	0.4

6 Name the solvent in all four brands.

7 Name two solutes in Pennine Spring water.

8 Which brand of water contains the most calcium?

9 Calculate the amount of potassium in 2 litres of Brecon Carreg water.

10 Sasha drinks half a litre of Volvic and half a litre of Pennine Spring. How much dissolved magnesium has she swallowed?

11 Mineral water must be bottled where it comes out of the ground, not taken in a tanker to be bottled elsewhere. Suggest why.

12 Describe an experiment you could do to measure the total mass of solid substances dissolved in a bottle of water.

Selling a promise?

An average Briton drinks about 26 litres of mineral water a year. There are many different brands, and each wants to persuade people to buy their brand – not someone else's. Here are some adverts.

13 How do each of the companies want you to feel about their products?

14 Why do you think that none of the advertisements mention taste?

15 Why do you think none of them mention the minerals they contain?

Get this

● Each spring gives water with different amounts of dissolved minerals.

Summing up

16 Explain how and why the water from each mineral water spring is different.

Watery dilemmas

Good for your heart?

Some mineral waters claim to be good for your health. But are they?

Roy has high blood pressure, which increases his risk of having a heart attack. Roy's doctor has read scientific articles suggesting that a lack of magnesium may cause high blood pressure. He tells Roy to eat foods rich in magnesium compounds, such as green vegetables.

Other scientists wondered if mineral water magnesium might also help reduce blood pressure. They designed a study to find out. They recruited 70 volunteers with slightly high blood pressure. They then took two readings of each volunteer's blood pressure, and calculated an average.

The scientists gave each volunteer one of these types of water:
- water low in minerals
- water with added magnesium compounds
- natural mineral water with high magnesium levels

The volunteers drank at least one litre of water every day. They did not know which type of water they had.

After four weeks, the scientists again measured the blood pressure of each volunteer. Overall, there was a decrease in blood pressure amongst the natural mineral water volunteers.

The scientists concluded that minerals in water, such as magnesium, may decrease blood pressure.

1 Why did the scientists take two blood pressure readings, and calculate an average?

2 Suggest why some volunteers drank water low in minerals.

3 Suggest why the volunteers were not told which type of water they had.

4 The scientists knew it would have been better to recruit more volunteers. Why is this? Why do you think they didn't?

5 One of the scientists works for a mineral water company. Does this affect your opinion of the research? Why?

Poison in the plastic?

Look on the bottom of most water bottles, and you'll see this symbol. It means the bottle is made from the plastic polyethylene terephthalate.

Learn about
- Researching health questions
- Making science decisions

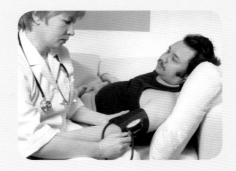

Scientist Bill Shotyk was worried about PET. Antimony trioxide is used to make it. Scientists suspect that antimony trioxide may increase the risk of cancer.

Shotyk measured the antimony **concentrations** of more than 60 mineral water brands. The measurements for one brand are in the table.

Row	Mineral water tested (all of the same brand)	Antimony concentration in nanogram/litre
1	Directly from the spring	3.8
2	In glass bottle, tested soon after buying	11.5
3	In PET bottle, tested soon after buying	359
4	In PET bottle, tested three months later	626

6 Which water has the lowest antimony concentration?

7 What conclusion can you make from the data in rows 2 and 3?

8 Which two rows of data support Shotyk's conclusion that, over time, more and more antimony moves from PET bottles into the water? Explain why.

Environmental evil

In 2008, a government minister said that drinking bottled water is 'bordering on the immoral'. Many environmental organisations agree with him. Here's why:

1. Plastic is made from oil. The process needs huge amounts of energy.

2. Plastic bottles are not **biodegradable**. Plastic waste ends up in landfill or is burned, which releases toxic chemicals into the air.

3. Water is very heavy. Transporting it hundreds of miles by ship and lorry burns fossil fuels and creates thousands of tonnes of carbon dioxide.

4. It is morally wrong to spend money on bottled water when millions of people do not have access to safe drinking water.

9 Decide on an order of importance for the four reasons above. Justify your choice.

10 Can science answer the question: Is it right to buy bottled water? Why?

Get this

- Scientists answer health questions by doing research.
- There are some questions that science cannot answer.

Summing up

11 Suggest some benefits of researching health questions.

How Science Works

Learn about
● Cleaning drinking water

Hurricane help

It's August 2005. Hurricane Katrina strikes the town of Waveland, Mississippi. Lives and homes are destroyed. Filthy water flows through broken pipes, and disease-causing microbes flourish. Survivors must walk 12 miles to buy bottled water.

Eventually, help arrives – on the back of a lorry. The Mobile Emergency Filtration System (MEFS) cleans up 200 000 litres of dirty water every day, enough for 10 000 people. Here's how it works.

- The water goes through a sand filter. Solids mixed with the water get stuck in the gaps between the sand grains.
- A centrifuge spins round and removes tiny bits of suspended solid.
- Ultraviolet radiation destroys bacteria and viruses.
- Ozone, O_3, destroys bacteria and viruses and breaks down pesticides.
- Tiny holes in an activated carbon filter trap molecules that cause bad tastes, smells and colours.

1 Which part of the MEFS removes dead spiders from the dirty water?

2 Which piece of equipment takes tiny pieces of soil from the water?

3 Why must bacteria and viruses be removed from drinking water?

4 How does the MEFS destroy bacteria?

5 How many oxygen atoms are in one ozone molecule?

The scientists who invented the MEFS plan to make smaller versions. They want them to go to disaster zones all over the world.

Water for your taps

How much water do you use each day? If you live in the UK, the answer is probably around 150 litres. That's enough to fill more than 12 big buckets. Assuming your water comes from the mains, it will all be safe to drink.

But the water doesn't start off clean. Water companies use techniques like those in the MEFS to remove dangerous and unpleasant impurities from water. Water companies may also add **chlorine** to kill bacteria or use microstrainers – huge rotating sieves – to remove solids and algae from the water.

6 Water from different sources needs different treatments. Work out which treatments to use for each water source below.

Water source 1: borehole

▲ Excellent water quality; occasionally contains bacteria.

Water source 2: reservoir

▲ Contains tiny bits of soil, algae, viruses and bacteria.

Water source 3: canal

▲ Contains algae, viruses and bacteria, pesticides, ammonia (which smells foul) and colour.

Water dilemmas

Jay does not drink tap water. He drinks bottled water because he thinks it is safer. He doesn't realise that water not labelled as mineral water – that's around 40% of bottled water – actually started out from the tap!

But *is* bottled water safer? In the USA, scientists tested more than 1000 bottles of 103 brands of bottled water. Bottles from more than thirty brands were contaminated by substances such as arsenic compounds or carcinogens (substances which increase the risk of cancer).

7 Do you think Jay's decision to drink only bottled water is a good one? Why?

Paula lives in London, and does not drink tap water. She drinks bottled mineral water because she wants to maximise her calcium intake. She spends about £1.60 on each litre of mineral water. Tap water costs less than 0.1 pence per litre.

8 How many litres of tap water could Paula buy for £1.60?

9 One litre of London tap water contains about 98 g of dissolved calcium. How does this value compare to those for the mineral water brands on page 89?

10 Do you think Paula's decision to drink only mineral water is sensible? Why?

Summing up

11 Create a table showing six different ways of treating water to make it safe to drink. Briefly describe what each method does, and how it works.

Get this

● Companies use filtering and chemicals to make safe drinking water.

Learn about
- Foams
- Accuracy and reliability

Sugar solubility

Shanice loves hot sweet tea. One day, she decides to make iced tea. How much sugar can dissolve in it? She does an experiment in science to find out.

Shanice measures out 100 cm³ water. She measures its temperature. She adds sugar and stirs until no more will dissolve. Then she records the mass of sugar added. She repeats the experiment twice more at this temperature, and takes an average. Then she does it all again at four different temperatures. Her results are in the table.

Most people in her class got similar results. This gave Shanice confidence that her data was reliable.

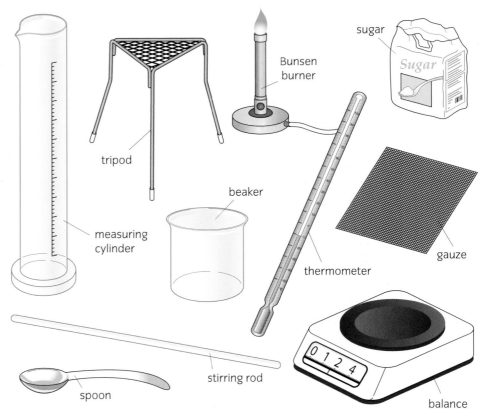

sugar

Bunsen burner

tripod

beaker

gauze

measuring cylinder

thermometer

stirring rod

spoon

balance

 1 How can Shanice make her experiment fair?

2 Why does repeating the experiment at each temperature help make the data accurate?

3 How else can Shanice make sure her data is as accurate as possible?

4 Calculate a value for the empty box in the table.

5 Shanice ignored her third result for 70 °C. Suggest why.

6 Plot the data on a graph. Draw a line of **best fit** (see page 142).

7 Write a conclusion to the experiment.

Temperature in °C	Mass of sugar that dissolves in 100 cm³ of water, in g			
	First time	Second time	Third time	Average
0	360	370	365	365
20	401	406	411	406
50	524	522	523	
70	647	647	500	647
100	957	961	953	957

Hot chocolate treat

Rob makes wonderful hot chocolate. Here's how…

First, Rob heats water in a kettle until it bubbles and steam comes out of the spout. He pours the hot water over instant hot chocolate powder in a mug, and stirs. The powder dissolves.

8 Why does Rob stir the mixture?

9 Name the change of state when liquid water becomes steam.

10 Draw two diagrams – one showing molecules in liquid water, the other showing molecules in steam.

11 Water's formula is H_2O. Name the elements that make up water. How many atoms of each of these elements are in one water molecule?

Next Rob adds spray cream. He shakes the can, holds it upside down and presses hard. The hot chocolate is covered in foamy cream. Yum!

What's in the foam?

Inside the can is a mixture of liquid cream, sugar and dinitrogen oxide gas, N_2O (laughing gas). The sugar and dinitrogen oxide are dissolved in the cream. As the mixture leaves the can, dinitrogen oxide molecules come out of solution. They spread out to form a gas. But they get trapped in the cream and form bubbles in it. The cream **foam** is made.

12 Is dinitrogen oxide **soluble** or **insoluble** in cream?

13 Copy and complete the diagram of the foam by drawing gas molecules inside the bubbles.

14 Spray cream floats on hot chocolate. Use the idea of density to explain why.

15 Rob sprays cream onto a plate. An hour later, the foam has gone down. Sweet liquid cream remains. What has happened to the dinitrogen oxide gas that was in the bubbles? Where are the sugar molecules?

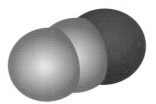

▲ An N_2O molecule

Summing up

16 Copy and complete: An _____ measurement is close to the true value. A _____ experiment gives very similar results if you repeat it

17 Explain how foam is formed.

Get this

- A solution is a mixture of a liquid with a solid or gas.
- Foams contain gas bubbles trapped in liquids or solids.

Learn about
- Calculating alcohol units
- Fermentation and distillation

What's in the glass?

Alcoholic drinks are mixtures of compounds. Molecules of **ethanol** (an **alcohol**), C_2H_5OH, make them alcoholic. Water fills up most of the rest of a bottle of beer or wine. Small amounts of other chemicals give drinks their different flavours.

In wine, these other chemicals include sweet sugars, sour acids and bitter and fruity tasting chemicals.

1　Name the three elements that make up the compound ethanol.

2　What type of chemical makes a drink sour?

How much alcohol?

Drinks contain different amounts of ethanol. A pint of beer contains about 30 cm³ ethanol. A glass of wine may contain 20 cm³ ethanol.

The 'alcohol by volume' (abv) figure on a bottle or can tells you what percentage of the mixture inside is ethanol. So in a 1000 cm³ bottle of wine with an abv of 10%, there is 100 cm³ of ethanol.

3　A 500 cm³ can of beer has an abv of 5%. What volume of ethanol does it contain?

Alcohol can kill. So people need to know how much they are drinking. A system of **units** helps drinkers work it out.

Here's how to calculate the units in a drink.
- Multiply its abv by the volume the person drinks.
- Divide the answer by 1000.

Jim drinks a pint (568 cm³) of cider. Its abv is 6%. The number of units is

$$(6 \times 568) \div 1000 = 3.4$$

4　Rose drinks a 175 cm³ glass of wine. Its abv is 14%. How many units is this?

No-one can be sure how much alcohol it is safe to drink. The government says that adult men can drink up to 3 or 4 units a day, and adult women up to 2 or 3 units. But in 2009 Oxford University scientists published evidence from a million women showing that just 1 unit a day increases the risk of cancer.

5　Do you think the government should change its advice because of this study? Why?

Making alcoholic drinks

Wine is made from grapes, and cider from apples. Both also use yeast. Yeast cells are microbes. They use fruit sugars as a source of energy, and make two waste products – carbon dioxide and ethanol.

The process is called **fermentation**. It works best at 37 °C.

Most wines, beers and ciders contain less than 15% alcohol. They are made by fermentation alone. Spirits, such as vodka and brandy, contain more alcohol. They are made by distillation.

Distillation involves heating a drink that was made by fermentation. At 79 °C, the ethanol in the drink boils and becomes a vapour. Water is left behind. The ethanol vapour is collected and cooled. It condenses, so you end up with a drink containing more alcohol than the original. For example, vodka is usually about 40% abv.

6 Charlotte drinks 25 cm³ of vodka of 40% abv. How many units is this?

7 Why do people drink spirits in much smaller quantities than wine or beer?

Drinking and driving

Every year, 3000 people are killed or seriously injured in crashes involving drink driving. Alcohol slows down the reactions in the brain, affects co-ordination and makes people reckless.

The maximum legal level of alcohol for driving is 80 milligrams of alcohol per 100 cm³ blood. But this is difficult to translate into units – how your body deals with alcohol depends on your age, sex, and weight.

8 Road safety charity Brake argues that people should not drink at all before driving. Do you think they are right? Why?

Get this

- Units show a drink's ethanol content.
- Fermentation makes alcoholic drinks.

Summing up

9 Create an advert explaining how to calculate alcohol units, and why it is important to drink sensibly – or not at all!

7.1 How far can we go?

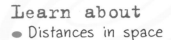

Through space and time

Dr Who can travel between **planets** in different galaxies in his Tardis, as well as backward and forward in time. At the moment, this technology is still science fiction.

But if anyone had suggested in 1900 that within 100 years people would have walked on the **Moon**, they would have been laughed at. Yet it was in 1969 that the first man walked on the Moon.

NASA has announced plans to send people back to the Moon by 2020. They will start work on a permanent Moon base. By 2037 NASA plans to land people on **Mars**.

Space distances

The Moon is the only natural **satellite** orbiting the Earth. It is in an **orbit** which is, on average, 385 000 km above the Earth. Rockets can travel at speeds of nearly 60 000 km/h.

 1 How long does it take for the fastest rocket to travel a distance similar to the distance from the Earth to the Moon? Choose from:

A half an hour   **B** two hours   **C** six hours
D twelve hours   **E** two days

Maximum speed

Nothing travels faster than light. Light from the Sun takes just over eight minutes to reach us. Light travels at 300 000 km/s, which means the Sun is about 149 000 000 km away.

 2 How long does it take for reflected light from the Moon to reach Earth?

A no time at all   **B** less than 1 s   **C** just over 1 s
D nearly 10 s

Some people estimate that by 2070, we will be able to travel through space at one per cent of the speed of light.

 3 How fast might we be travelling through space after 2070?

Nearest neighbours

Neptune is the furthest planet from the Sun in our Solar System. Light from the Sun takes over four hours to reach Neptune. Voyager 2 was launched on 20 August 1977 but it was not until 12 years later, on 25 August 1989 that it passed Neptune.

Reach for the stars

The Sun is the nearest **star** to Earth. The next nearest star to Earth is called Proxima Centauri.

Proxima Centauri is 40 000 000 000 000 km away. Light from Proxima Centauri takes 4.3 years to reach us. Scientists measure these large distances in units called **light years**. This is the distance light travels in one year.

4 How far away, in light years, is Proxima Centauri?

Our Solar System is near the edge of the Milky Way **galaxy**. This galaxy contains maybe 400 billion stars. The width of the Milky Way is between 70 and 100 thousand light years.

5 How long does it take for light to travel from one side of the Milky Way to the other?

The fastest rocket to leave the Earth is travelling towards Pluto at a speed of 58 000 km/h.

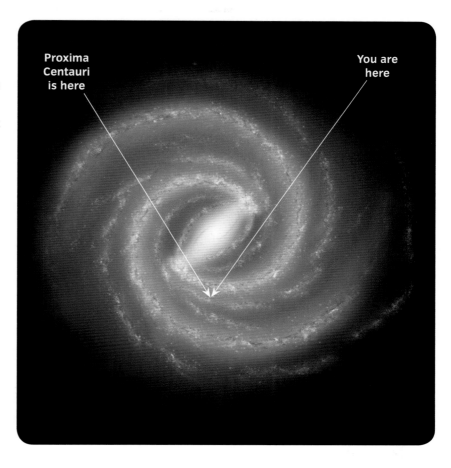

Proxima Centauri is here

You are here

At that speed, it would take

1 300 000 000 Earth years

just to travel across the Milky Way.

Scientists estimate that beyond the Milky Way are at least 100 billion more galaxies. Each galaxy contains billions of stars. The furthest star we have seen is 15 billion light years away.

That's about 142 000 000 000 000 billion km.

Summing up

6 Which of the planets in our Solar System receives light from the Sun in the shortest time?

7 If we could travel at 1% of the speed of light in 2070, approximately how long would it take to reach Neptune?

Get this

- Distances in space are very large.
- Scientists use light years as a measure of distance.
- It takes a long time to reach even the nearest planets.

Learn about
- Staying in orbit
- Conditions on the Moon

Journey to the Moon

Apollo 11 left Earth in July 1969 with Neil Armstrong, Buzz Aldrin and Michael Collins on board. It was just over three days before it started to orbit the Moon. It stayed in orbit a further 26 hours before starting its one hour descent to the lunar surface.

Each orbit took two hours.

 1 How many times did Apollo 11 orbit the Moon before starting to land?

'One small step...'

'...for man, one giant leap for mankind.' These were Neil Armstrong's words as he stepped onto the surface of the Moon on 20 July 1969.

 2 What did he mean by these words?

3 Forty years after that first moon landing do you think he was right?

One of the first things Neil Armstrong did was to report on the lunar surface:

'The surface is fine and powdery. I can kick it up loosely with my toe. I only go in a small fraction of an inch, maybe an eighth of an inch, but I can see the footprints of my boots and the treads in the fine sandy particles.'

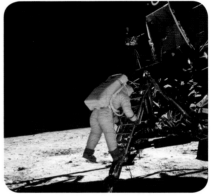

There is **gravity** on the Moon, but its strength is only one sixth of that on Earth. This is one reason why the moon has no **atmosphere**. Gases are not held down to the Moon's surface so they can easily escape into space. The Moon's surface is almost a vacuum.

Without an atmosphere, the Moon also has no climate. There is no wind, no rain, no storms, no floods and no fires. The surface of the Moon is only affected by things such as meteors hitting the surface.

 4 What causes craters on the Moon?

With no atmosphere, there is no oxygen to breathe and no **air pressure** (no **atmospheric pressure**). On Earth the air pressing down all over our bodies stops them swelling up dangerously. The Earth's atmosphere traps some of the Sun's warmth and warms the planet. It blocks some of the harmful **ultraviolet (UV) radiation** from the Sun.

So, unlike Wallace and Gromit, astronauts on the Moon have to wear spacesuits.

Spacesuits provide astronauts with oxygen and keep their body temperature constant. They protect them from UV radiation and stop them being hurt by flying space debris.

 5 Spacesuits are also pressurised. Why?

Falling constantly

How does a spacecraft stay in orbit around the Moon or the Earth?

If you step off the diving board, you will fall straight down. If you run off the diving board, you will land further out. The faster you run, the further out you will land.

If you could run fast enough, you would land beyond the horizon because the Earth is curved.

Run faster still and you will constantly fall to Earth as the Earth falls away from you – you are in orbit.

Spacecraft in a low orbit are travelling at speeds of about 8 km/s and take 90 minutes to orbit the Earth. This is what Apollo 11 did before it set off for the Moon.

 6 Imagine you could run at 8 km/s and survive. What would happen if you did this from the top of a very high diving platform?

7 What did Apollo 11 do before landing on the Moon? Choose from:
A speed up
B slow down
C steer towards the Moon's surface at the same speed

Get this

- If an object is travelling fast enough, it will stay in orbit.
- The Moon has a gravitational field.
- The Moon does not have an atmosphere.

Summing up

8 Explain why the boot print made by Buzz Aldrin is still there.

9 When Wallace kicked the ball up, it did not come back down. What happens on the Moon if an astronaut kicks a ball up?

Gravity pulls

Gravitational fields

All objects are surrounded by **gravitational fields**. The strength of a gravitational field depends on the **mass** of the object. The more massive the object, the stronger its gravitational field.

When British Olympic diver, Tom Daley, leaves the 10 m platform, there is a force of attraction between him and the Earth.

Learn about
- Weight, mass and gravity
- Gravity and space

 1 Why does Tom move towards the Earth and not the Earth towards Tom?

The gravitational force of attraction towards the Earth is called **weight**. Weight is measured in newtons (N). On Earth, a mass of 1 kg weighs 10 N.

 2 How much does a 72 kg astronaut weigh on Earth?

The gravitational force of attraction on other planets is different. The larger the mass of the planet, the bigger the gravitational force. The diagram shows what our 72 kg astronaut would weigh on other planets.

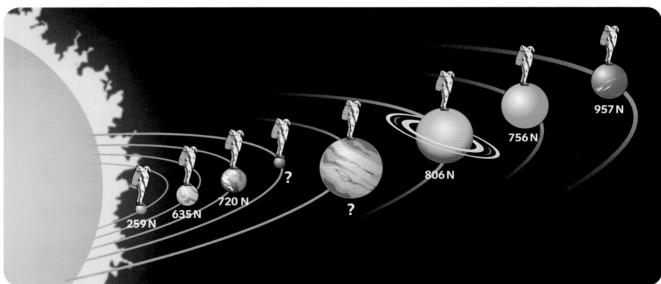

259 N 635 N 720 N ? ? 806 N 756 N 957 N

Jupiter's mass is at least three hundred times the mass of Earth. The force of gravity on the surface is 2.5 times that of Earth.

3 How much would the 72 kg astronaut weigh on Jupiter?

Mars has a mass that is just one-tenth the mass of Earth. The force of gravity on the surface is 0.4 times that of Earth.

4 How much would the 72 kg astronaut weigh on Mars?

Out in space

As astronauts get further away from Earth, the gravitational force attracting them back to Earth gets smaller. The further an object is away from the centre of a planet, the smaller the gravitational force.

Helen Sharman was the first of only four Britons who have been in space. She knows how gravitational force changes as you get further away from the Earth:

'The important thing to remember is that gravity is always there. Without gravity, I could not have returned to Earth from the Space Station I was working on. Gravity is not something you can switch on and off like they do in cartoons. Even hundreds of kilometres from Earth, when you feel weightless in the space station, there is still some gravitational force attracting you back towards Earth.

Think about how you feel in a fast lift as it accelerates downwards. You feel a lot lighter. If the lift is falling freely, you feel weightless. A spacecraft orbiting the Earth is also falling freely through space. It never falls back to Earth because the Earth is falling away underneath the spacecraft as it orbits. So the astronauts inside feel weightless.

Because there is always some gravity, you can never actually be weightless.'

The astronaut Jeffrey Hoffman describes returning to Earth:

*'I enjoy the last few minutes of weightlessness, spinning my camera as it floats in front of my face. The **deceleration** is minute, but I notice that my camera is moving very slowly towards the floor. I pick it up and place it once again in front of my face, only to see it move downward a little bit faster than the last time. Even stranger, I realise that my hands are now resting on my lap instead of floating in front of me as I have become used to seeing during our time in orbit.'*

Get this

- An object's gravitational force depends on its mass.
- An object's gravitational force decreases as the distance away from it increases.
- Satellites stay in orbit because of gravitational attraction.
- Astronauts feel weightless but gravity is still acting on them.

Summing up

5 A 72 kg astronaut weighs 720 N on Earth. He is in a spacecraft orbiting the Earth. He stands on a set of bathroom scales. What is the reading on the scales?

6 Jeffrey Hoffman describes how his camera falls faster towards the floor as his spacecraft gets closer to Earth. Why does it fall faster?

Learn about
- Exploring space from space

A new view

People have been looking at the Moon and stars for thousands of years. But **astronomers** using equipment on Earth cannot see clearly things that are far away in space. The atmosphere makes images very blurred. Pollution also makes things difficult to see.

Once we put satellites into space, we could see things more clearly and see things we had never seen before.

 1 Look at the photograph of Europe taken from space at night. What type of pollution makes it difficult to see stars at night?

2 Why are pictures of objects in space, taken from satellites, clearer than those taken from Earth?

The Moon spins on its axis at the same rate as it orbits the Earth. This means the same side of the Moon is facing Earth all the time. In 1959, a Russian satellite took this first picture of the other side of the Moon.

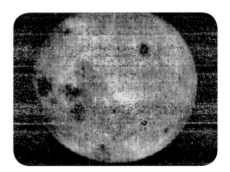

Maintaining Hubble

The Hubble Space Telescope orbits the Earth. It is a medium sized telescope. Its mirror is only 240 cm across. But it takes very detailed pictures of the Universe, not only in our Solar System but also of stars more than 13 billion light years away. This is because of the high quality of its instruments and its position above the atmosphere.

 3 What is a light year?

In 2005, it was predicted that Hubble would stop working by the end of 2010 because the batteries would fail. However, a servicing mission is planned for 2009 that will keep Hubble functioning for at least a further four years.

During the first servicing mission in 1993, astronauts replaced Hubble's main camera. It has a mass of 277 kg on Earth. It can detect stars a billion times fainter than the ones we can see with our eyes.

 4 What is the mass of Hubble's camera in space?

5 What is the weight, in newtons, of Hubble's camera on Earth?

6 How much does Hubble's camera appear to weigh in space?

New discoveries

In November 2008, Hubble took the first photograph of a planet orbiting a star outside our own Solar System. In a star system 25 light years away from us, the planet, known as Fomalhaut b, orbits its parent star Fomalhaut.

Many space discoveries are made by looking at the unusual behaviour of things we can see and predicting what causes such behaviour. The behaviour of the dust around the star Fomalhaut suggested that it was being affected by the gravity of an orbiting planet.

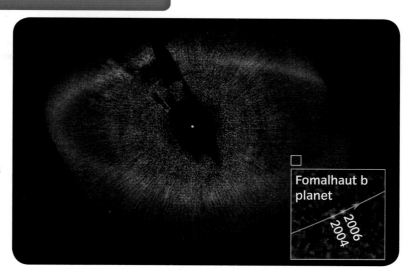

Fomalhaut b planet

2006
2004

Scientists observed the star and its dust cloud over a two-year period from 2004 to 2006. They pinpointed the likely path of the planet's orbit. Finally, in 2008, Hubble managed to photograph the planet itself which is one billion times dimmer than its star.

7 Why was it so difficult to spot Fomalhaut b?

8 Why did scientists predict that it was there?

The next generation

A new orbiting satellite will be launched in 2013. The James Webb Space Telescope will orbit more than 1.5 million kilometres above Earth, beyond the Moon's orbit. It will be able to see even further and in more detail than Hubble.

The Webb telescope will take pictures using **infrared** radiation instead of light. Infrared radiation can pass through dust clouds in space, unlike light. Some objects in space are too cool to emit enough **visible light** to be seen, but they emit infrared radiation that can be detected.

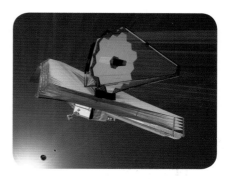

▲ Artist's impression of the new Webb telescope.

9 What advantage does the Webb telescope have over the Hubble telescope?

Get this

- The Earth's atmosphere makes it difficult to see distant objects in space.
- Telescopes outside the Earth's atmosphere provide clearer pictures.
- Telescopes using infrared radiation provide clearer pictures still.

Summing up

10 How do space telescopes help to increase our understanding of space?

11 When we look at distant objects in space, we see the history of the Universe. Explain why.

Learn about
- Living in space

'I see Earth. It's so beautiful'

These were the first words spoken from space by the Russian cosmonaut Yuri Gagarin, who orbited the Earth in 1961.

The Soviet Union had beaten the United States in the race to send a human into space. In 1961 the Soviet Union (Russia and the countries linked with it) and the United States were enemies in the 'Cold War'.

The space race went on. Americans were first on the Moon; the Russians were the first to start building a space station.

But, in 1989, a huge political change happened in the Soviet Union and the Cold War ended. America and Russia were both struggling to find the huge amounts of money needed for space exploration. They joined forces and together with Canada, Japan, and 11 European countries are building a truly international space station.

International Space Station

The International Space Station (ISS) was started in November 1998 when a Russian built module was launched into orbit. A few weeks later a second, American, module was bolted on.

From 1998 to 2008, there were a further 28 missions, to add further modules.

The ISS is the largest spacecraft ever built. Its area is larger than a football pitch.

The first crew moved into the station in 2000. Since then, 167 men and women from 15 countries have visited the station. Most stay for between four and six months. There are always between three and ten people on board.

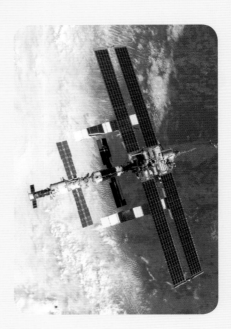

? **1** Why has the ISS been built in modules rather than being sent into space all at once?

2 How does the International Space Station get its electricity?

Living in space

Karen Nyberg looks back at the Earth from the International Space Station.

In June 2008, she spent 13 days aboard the ISS. Her time in space was very different from Yuri Gagarin's. Yuri spent just 108 minutes in space. He wore his space suit the whole time and was strapped into his tiny spacecraft, which was a sphere 230 cm in diameter.

3 Describe three differences between Nyberg's and Gagarin's trips to space.

We have learned a lot from the Space Station about living in space. The oxygen needed for the astronauts living on the ISS cannot be delivered constantly from Earth. The Station must make most of its oxygen. Water is split into hydrogen and oxygen using electricity from the station's solar cells.

There is water vapour in the air we breathe out. The water astronauts breathe out is recycled back into the system to be used again. Their urine is also purified and recycled.

 4 Why can water be split into hydrogen and oxygen?

5 What else do astronauts breathe out?

An orbiting laboratory

There have been well over 1000 experiments done on board the Space Station during the past ten years – many of which have helped us on Earth.

For example, gravity affects the way in which crystals grow. Crystals grown in the Space Station make better semiconductors for faster computers and more efficient drugs to combat diseases.

There are also experiments which will help if we want to build a colony on the Moon or on Mars. To make enough oxygen for a colony we will need to grow plants. But plants rely on Earth's gravity to know which way to send out shoots and roots. Gravity on Mars is much weaker than on Earth which makes plants harder to grow. Scientists working on the Space Station are investigating how to make them grow in low gravity conditions like the plant here.

 6 How do plants produce oxygen?

Summing up

7 Some people say that money spent on experiments in space could be better spent on other things. Should we experiment in space? Explain the reasons for your answer.

Get this

- The ISS is only possible because of the cooperation of many countries.
- Experiments on the ISS will help us on Earth and in establishing bases on the Moon or Mars.

Moonbase 2020

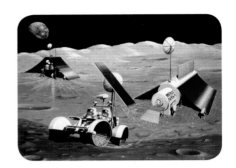

Back to the Moon

It is more than 30 years since the last astronauts walked on the Moon. The first landing in 1969 was exciting but by 1972, when the last one took place, people were losing interest. There didn't seem to be anything useful on the Moon and the missions were expensive.

Now the United States plans to return astronauts to the Moon by 2020. Work will start on a permanent base there. By 2024, astronauts will be staying up to six months at the Moon base.

Russia is also talking about a base on the Moon. China plans to send astronauts there by 2017.

How will people live on the Moon? NASA is sending a Reconnaissance Orbiter in 2009. It will look for safe landing sites, and will try to find out whether there is water, or hydrogen, trapped on the Moon. Ilmenite is a common mineral found on the Moon. This contains oxygen which can be extracted from it.

 1 Why are conditions on the Moon difficult for humans?

2 What essential chemical could be made, on the Moon, from trapped hydrogen and the oxygen in ilmenite?

Exploring space

But why go back to this bare and hostile lump of rock? Space exploration is one answer.

The Moonbase will include an observatory.

A large radio dish, set into the lunar surface, will collect radio signals from stars and other bodies in space. Computers and astronomers will analyse the signals to provide information about the body, just like an observatory on Earth.

 3 What is the main advantage of having an observatory on the Moon instead of on Earth?

4 What would be the advantages of a lunar observatory over the Hubble Space Telescope?

Some of the conditions on the Moon are harsher than those on Mars. By working on the Moon, astronauts will be preparing for future exploration to Mars and beyond. If anything goes wrong it only takes two or three days for a rescue mission to reach the Moon but it takes six months to get to Mars!

Energy for Earth?

Recent scientific advances also mean that we might be able to use the Moon to solve our energy problems on the Earth. One way would be to harness sunlight. The Sun's energy travels as electromagnetic waves through space. Light, infrared radiation and ultraviolet radiation are all electromagnetic waves.

The Earth's atmosphere stops a lot of the available energy in sunlight from getting through to the surface. For example, the ozone layer stops harmful amounts of ultraviolet radiation getting through.

The Moon has no atmosphere so it receives all of the radiation from the Sun. This could then be converted into another form of **electromagnetic radiation**, **microwaves**. The microwave radiation could be beamed to the Earth. Unlike sunlight, microwaves can easily pass through rain, clouds, dust and smoke.

Some scientists think that by 2050 enough lunar solar power could be sent to the Earth to supply the whole of the world's population of 10 billion people.

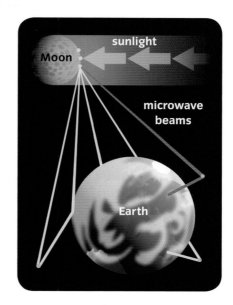

 5 Why can electromagnetic waves, like light, travel through space but sound waves can't?

6 Why is it important that the atmosphere stops a lot of the Sun's energy getting through to Earth?

Energy from helium

Some of the rocks on the Moon contain types of elements and minerals which are very rare on Earth. One of these is a form of helium called helium-3. Some experts say that there are millions of tonnes of helium-3 in the lunar soil.

Scientists do not always agree about the best solutions to a problem.

 7 What are the arguments for and against using helium-3 from the Moon on Earth?

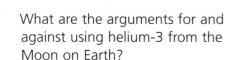

- A permanent base on the Moon could:
  - help space exploration
  - help the Earth's energy crisis

Summing up

8 Why have scientists and governments started to think that the Moon could be useful?

9 Why can more energy be obtained from sunlight on the Moon than from sunlight on Earth?

Exploring Mars

Early days

In 1965, Mariner 4 was the first spacecraft to successfully fly past Mars. But astronomers had been intrigued by Mars for centuries.

Three hundred years earlier, the Dutch astronomer, Christiaan Huygens, wrote Cosmotheoros, a book about whether or not there is life on Mars.

During the 1600s, astronomers had already worked out that the fourth planet from the Sun was more like Earth than any other planet. They had seen mountains and valleys; ice caps at its poles; volcanoes. They knew its day length is only 39 minutes 35 seconds longer than Earth's but that a year on Mars lasts 687 Earth days.

In 1784, the British astronomer William Herschel told the Royal Society that the changes of bright and dark patches across the surface of Mars suggested '*clouds and vapours floating in the atmosphere of the planet.*' He concluded:

'*Mars has a considerable but modest atmosphere, so that its inhabitants probably enjoy a situation in many respects similar to our own.*'

1 Why did Herschel think Mars had an atmosphere?

2 Why did scientists in the 1600s and 1700s think there might be life on Mars?

Go take a look

Between 1960 and 1975, America and the USSR made more than twenty attempts to send spacecraft to Mars. There were many failures. Some did not even leave the launch pad; some lost contact during the six month journey.

Mariner 4 was in flyby mode and sent back the first close-up pictures of the Martian surface. They showed a Moon-like cratered terrain. Later missions showed that this was not typical.

Instruments measured a very low surface atmospheric pressure, which means that the atmosphere is very thin. They also found that the atmosphere was almost totally carbon dioxide. Daytime temperatures were estimated to be −100 °C.

3 By flying past Mars, what information did Mariner 4 get that could not be measured from Earth?

4 What did Mariner 4 confirm about previous observations?

In 1971, the USSR put two spacecraft in orbit around Mars and America put one. Mariner 9 photographed the entire surface of the planet. This confirmed gigantic volcanoes and a grand canyon stretching 4800 kilometres. There appeared to be the remains of ancient riverbeds carved in the landscape, but very few craters.

 5 Why was data from the orbiter Mariner 9 more reliable than data from Mariner 4?

From the surface

In 1975, America launched two Viking spacecraft which both landed successfully and sent back high quality pictures of the surface. They also examined the atmosphere and looked at the surface for evidence of life. They analysed soil from the two landing sites and they found no microorganisms. This did not prove that life does not exist, because only two small samples were taken from the whole planet.

Between 1988 and 2005, there were 15 more missions. From these launches, six spacecraft ended up in orbit around Mars and four landed on the surface. Three rovers went out onto the surface, the first in 1997 to gather data.

In 2004, two rovers were landed on the surface of Mars on a three-month mission. Nearly five years later they were still transmitting valuable data. In November 2008, one of the rovers was 'retired'. In the middle of the Martian winter, it was covered in dust and was not charging its batteries fully every day.

 6 Suggest two reasons why batteries on the rover were not being fully charged.

7 What advantages do rovers have over probes that stay in one place?

off the mark.com   by Mark Parisi

WE'RE SAFE... MYRAXX IS USING PHOTOSHOP TO DELETE US FROM ALL THE IMAGES...

©2004 MARK PARISI DIST. BY UFS, INC.   offthemark.com

Summing up

8 What effects have developments in technology had on our data and theories about Mars?

9 Describe the difficulties scientists face in gathering reliable data from Mars.

Get this

- Astronomers knew a lot about Mars, even before spacecraft were sent there.
- Mars is the planet most like Earth.

111

Ice is nice

This was the excited blog from NASA scientist Patrick Woida after the Phoenix landing craft had reported back the disappearance of solid lumps from a trench dug by its robotic arm. At first, scientists thought the lumps might be salt, but when they disappeared after only a four-day interval the conclusion is that it must be water ice.

In 2000, scientists began to suspect that there was, or had been quite recently, water on Mars. The gullies, shown in this photograph, may have been formed from water coming to the surface.

Other photographs of the same area, taken by an orbiting satellite, over a period of time, show a gully in 2005 that was not there in 1999.

In March 2008, Phoenix also discovered salt deposits which scientists think came from groundwater reaching the surface in low spots and then evaporating.

1 What evidence did scientists have before 2008 of water under the Martian surface?

2 How did data from the Phoenix lander add to this evidence?

3 Why are scientists excited at the possibility of finding water on Mars?

Ancient life

It might look like any old lump of rock, but the **meteorite**, ALH84001, tells the story of life on Mars.

4 What is a meteorite?

It was found in Antarctica on 27 December 1984, and had been lying there for the past 13 000 years. It was probably dislodged from the surface of Mars when a large meteorite struck it 16 million years ago.

Under a microscope, it appeared to have the fossilised remains of bacteria from over 3 billion years ago.

Compounds of carbon, called carbonates, were found in the rock. These carbonates are similar to those found in rocks on Earth, like limestone, which are formed when microorganisms die and decay.

5 What evidence is there that there may have been microorganisms on Mars?

Learn about
- The possibility of finding life on Mars
- Whether a Mars colony is possible

Ice is Nice!!!!
by Patrick Woida

June 20, 2008 -
Well, after weeks of talking about 'white stuff,' we're finally ready to call the 'unknown white substance that we are guardedly optimistic is ice but could be salt' ICE, and it could not be much else.

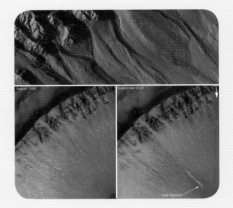
ALH84001,0

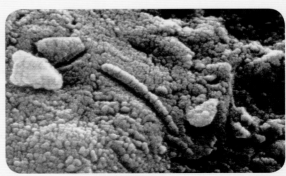

In January 2009, NASA confirmed that **methane** was being produced on Mars. Methane comes from waste products from living things or geological activity. The amount of methane appears to be changing yearly, but there are no signs of geological activity.

The next mission to Mars is planned for 2011. One of its main aims will be to look for further evidence of life, either past or present.

 6 Why might the presence of methane be evidence for life on Mars?

Terraforming Mars

Terraforming is the process of making a planet more Earthlike so we can live there. It would take hundreds of years to do this on Mars.

The southern polar ice cap contains a lot of carbon dioxide. If this could be melted then the amount of carbon dioxide in the atmosphere would increase. The whole planet would get warmer by the greenhouse effect.

 7 How would raising the temperature help us to live on Mars?

8 What else would we have to change on Mars if we were to live there?

Our bodies would need to get used to the lower gravity and we would need to be aware of some possible psychological problems.

On Earth, we are used to communicating with people almost instantly – even if they are the far side of the world. But a message sent to Mars will not be received for ten minutes and it will be another ten minutes before we get an answer.

There is also no instant help in an emergency – Earth is a six-month flight away. If astronauts visit Mars within the next 50 years they will have to deal with these problems.

Summing up

9 Explain why scientists think that Mars may have supported life in the past.

10 In what two ways could the carbon dioxide on Mars help us change it to support life?

Get this

- Mars is the planet most like Earth.
- There is evidence that Mars has water and may have supported life.

113

Energy sources

Cliff railways

Cliff railways are used all over the world to move people and goods up and down steep cliffs.

Two parallel tracks carry two passenger cars, one on each. The two cars are attached to each other by a cable, which runs through a pulley at the top of the slope. As one car goes up the other goes down.

Energy is needed to move the cars. In the case of this railway in Bournemouth it is mostly **electrical energy**.

Water power

But there are other energy sources. The Lynton Railway uses *only* water power to carry people and goods between the villages of Lynmouth, on the North Devon coast, and Lynton about 170m vertically above it. It is unique.

How does it work?

- When each car is docked with one at the top and one at the bottom, their water tanks are full.
- When passengers have boarded, the drivers exchange signals and the driver at the bottom empties his water tank.
- This means that the top car is now heavier so it moves downwards and pulls the lower car up the cliff.
- The water comes from a reservoir at the top of the cliff, fed from the River Lyn.

1 Suggest how the drivers can control the speed of the cars.

2 Sam said that gravity moved the cars. Explain what he meant.

Energy transfers

The **gravitational potential energy** of the water in the tank of the car at the top of the cliff is the energy source for the water-powered railway at Lynton and Lynmouth. This is stored energy.

It is transferred to **kinetic energy** as the car descends. It also transfers kinetic energy to the less heavy car that is connected to it. As this car rises up the cliff it gains gravitational potential energy.

3 Why doesn't this cliff railway need any electrical energy?

In clifftop lifts, which mostly use electrical energy, the gravitational potential energy of the car going down is still important. It helps to reduce the amount of electrical energy needed.

Electrical energy is transferred to other forms of energy through a device like a motor or a light bulb. A motor changes electrical energy to kinetic energy. It also produces unwanted energy forms – thermal energy (heat) and sound. We can show this in an energy transfer diagram.

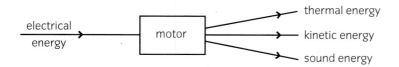

One of the jobs of this lift at Sennen Cove in Cornwall is to move the dustbin from the road to the house at the top.

 4 Draw an energy transfer diagram for the lift.

Sources of energy

Inside electrical devices an **electric current** carries energy around a circuit. The current is *not* used up. It returns to the battery or mains supply to collect more energy to go round the circuit again.

The energy in a battery is also stored energy and is called chemical energy.

Summing up

5 Name five things that need energy to make them work.

6 Energy is often wasted due to friction. What forms does this wasted energy take?

7 How do cliff railways minimise the energy needed to lift the ascending car?

8 Early railways used steam power. What was their energy source? What fuel did they use?

Get this

- Energy is transferred from one form to another.
- Chemical energy and gravitational potential energy are stored energy.
- Electrical energy is transferred by devices.
- An electrical current carries energy.

Learn about
● Renewable energy
● Solar energy

Indian Ocean

REUNION

Life on a tropical island

The Lescaux family live in a village on Reunion, a small French island close to Africa.

It is roughly the size of London but with a much smaller population.

The island's chief crop is sugar and M. Lescaux works on a sugar cane plantation. Until recently, electricity was very expensive and it is still not available in some remote villages.

Electricity used to be generated on Reunion only using oil, which is a fossil fuel. But oil has to be imported so it is expensive. It can also cause pollution.

So, in 2004, the government decided to invest in **renewable** energy sources which are available on the island. Reunion averages 1350 hours of sunshine each year so **solar energy** plays a large part in its plans.

? 1   What is meant by 'renewables'?

2   Why are renewables better than oil for producing electricity?

In 2008, the island made around 45% of its electricity from 'renewables' and plans to be energy self-sufficient by 2025.

? 3   Suggest what '**energy self-sufficient**' means.

Solar energy

The Sun supplies energy in the form of heat and light. Its energy can be used

● to heat water directly in **solar panels**;
● to produce electricity using **solar cells**, also known as **photocells**.

The Lescaux family plan to put solar panels like these on the roof of their house to provide hot water.

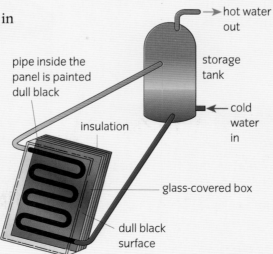

pipe inside the panel is painted dull black

insulation

glass-covered box

dull black surface

hot water out

storage tank

cold water in

4 Draw an energy transfer diagram for a solar panel.

5 Why are the pipes usually made of copper?

6 Why are the pipes painted black?

The Lescaux family also decide to install photocells to provide them with electricity. A photocell transfers light energy into electrical energy. Your calculator probably gets its energy from a photocell.

The amount of electricity photocells produce depends on the area of their surface exposed to sunlight. An area of 1 m² can produce up to 50 W of electrical power. This would be enough for the Lescaux children to power a laptop, something they dream of owning.

The photocells will charge a **battery**. This stores electrical energy so will give them electricity at night or during bad weather. Even on Reunion the Sun does not always shine!

 7 Why are photocells a good way of providing electricity in remote areas?

8 What is the minimum area of photocells that would be needed to run a 2000 W washing machine?

More energy

Energy from wind power and biomass (from sugar cane waste) are also used on Reunion but solar energy is the main renewable energy source.

A large solar power plant has been built on Reunion Island with photocells covering 10 000 m².

This, together with electricity from other renewable sources, will provide more than the island needs. It can sell the extra to the French electricity supplier EDF, and make a profit from the sale of green electricity.

▲ Close-up of a sugar cane stalk

 9 Estimate how many laptops could be run from this large solar power plant.

10 Suggest why it is called green electricity.

Summing up

11 Why is Reunion Island particularly suitable for solar energy?

12 Draw an energy transfer diagram for a photocell.

13 Give two advantages of using photocells to provide electricity.

14 Give one disadvantage of using photocells to provide electricity.

Get this
- Renewable energy sources can be replaced, unlike fuels.
- Solar energy is a major energy source in hot countries.

HOW Science WORKS

Learn about
- Wind energy
- Hydro-electric energy

Life on a Scottish island

The McKay family lives on the tiny Hebridean island of Eigg. The island is 9 km long and 5 km wide, with a population of about 70. It is mountainous with a lot of windy weather and limited sunshine.

Mr and Mrs McKay run a small farm, or croft.

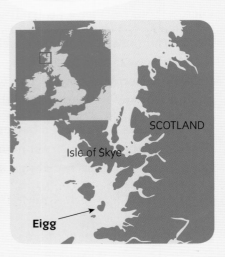

SCOTLAND

Isle of Skye

Eigg

There was no mains supply of electricity until 2008. The family relied on a small diesel-powered **generator** for electricity. The fuel had to be brought over by boat but in rough weather the service was often cancelled.

Each morning Mrs McKay had to go outside to crank the generator into life by hand. They did not bother with it just for light, using candles instead. The constant thudding noise from their generator could be heard for miles.

The McKay family considered installing photocells to produce electricity. They decided against it. The amount of electricity produced would be too small compared with the installation costs.

1 Why did the McKays think photocells would not produce much electricity?

Wind turbines

Some Eigg residents had installed small **wind turbines** to provide electricity.

The wind turns the blades of the wind turbine. This turns a generator which produces electricity. In this way the kinetic energy of the wind is transferred to electrical energy.

Wind power is a renewable resource and does not produce any polluting waste. But the residents still needed a diesel generator.

2 Why do wind turbines work well on Eigg?

3 Why did residents need a diesel generator as well as a wind turbine?

A new energy grid

How did Eigg get its mains electricity supply in 2008? Laying a cable across the sea from the power stations on the mainland was much too expensive. A fossil fuel power station on the island was also too expensive and would mean bringing fuel in by sea.

The answer was a combination of the renewable energy sources available on the island: hydro-electric, wind and solar.

Hydro-electric power uses water released from a high reservoir. Mountains provide ideal locations for these reservoirs. When the water falls, its gravitational potential energy is transferred to kinetic energy. This turns a generator to produce electrical energy.

This system can supply more than 95% of Eigg's annual energy needs. When one source is not providing much energy (eg there's no wind) the others will keep up the supply. It is backed up by a battery storage system and two diesel generators in case of an emergency.

Each house and business can only use a set amount of electricity each day. If they exceed this limit their meter 'locks-out' and they have to pay a fine.

The project employs local people who service, maintain and repair the systems.

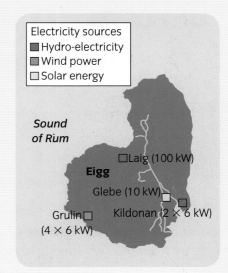

 4 Look at the map. Which renewable source produces most power?

5 How much electrical power is supplied altogether by the three sources?

6 Why is a battery storage system needed?

Mrs McKay was delighted to be able to have a washing machine and a vacuum cleaner. She used to have to wash everything by hand.

7 Suggest two things the McKay children wanted when mains electricity came to Eigg.

Summing up

8 Why did the McKay family decide not to install photocells on their croft?

9 Why can the people on Eigg only use a certain amount of electricity each day?

10 Describe the differences which the new technologies have made to the life of people on Eigg.

Get this

- In some places a combination of renewable resources is needed to provide reliable electricity.

Making electricity

What do generators do?

Most methods of making electricity use energy to turn a **turbine**. A turbine has blades and spins when blasted with steam or air or water. The turbine turns a generator. The generator makes electricity.

Most power stations still use non-renewable fuels to heat water to make steam to turn a turbine.

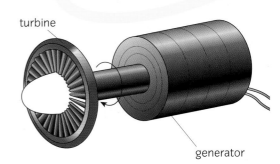

turbine

generator

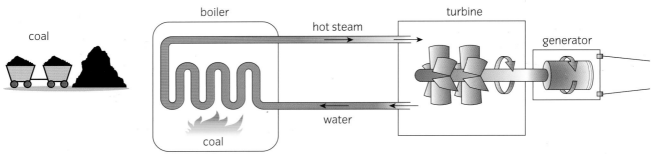

coal

boiler

hot steam

turbine

generator

coal

water

 1   Name three non-renewable fuels used in this way.

Most renewable energy systems also turn a turbine but they do not generally use steam to turn it.

 2   What energy source does a wind turbine use?

3   What energy source does a hydro-electric power station use?

Photocells do not use a turbine or generator. They transfer light energy from the Sun directly to electrical energy.

Making electricity

Electricity flowing through a wire forms a **magnetic field** around the wire. Electromagnets are made using electricity flowing through a coil of wire.

We also use magnets and wire to make electricity. If you move a magnet inside or near a coil of wire you can make electricity flow through the wire.

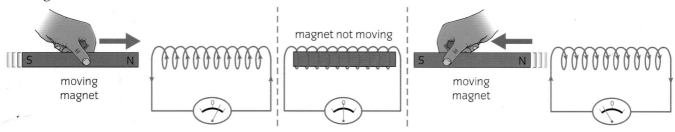

moving magnet

magnet not moving

moving magnet

A **voltage** is also made, or **induced**, if the coil moves and the magnet stays still. But one of them has to move. The coil of wire has to cut across the magnetic field of the magnet.

 4 Sketch the magnetic field around a bar magnet.

A bigger voltage is induced if the magnet or coil move faster, a stronger magnet is used or there are more turns on the coil. Each of these changes means more magnetic field lines are cut each second.

How do generators work?

A simple generator uses a spinning magnet to transfer kinetic energy to electrical energy. A rotating turbine is connected to a magnet, making it spin.

This type of generator was used by the people of Eigg before they got mains electricity. A very small generator like this, called a **dynamo**, is also used to power the lights on Tim's bicycle.

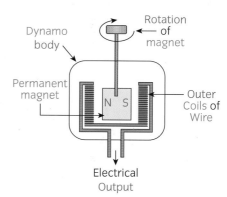

 5 How does Tim make the magnet spin?

6 What can he do to make the lights brighter?

Power station generators

The generators used in power stations are huge.

They use electromagnets instead of permanent magnets. Electromagnets can be made stronger than permanent magnets. This induces a bigger voltage. Electromagnets are made by passing an electric current through a coil of wire wound on an **iron core**.

 7 Why is the coil wound on an iron core?

8 How can an electromagnet be made stronger?

Small generators with permanent magnets produce the electricity for the electromagnets. But they use much less energy than the large generators produce.

Summing up

9 What is the main energy transfer that takes place in a generator?

10 Give three ways in which the induced voltage in a generator can be made bigger.

11 Why are electromagnets used instead of permanent magnets in a power station generator?

12 Why do bikes usually have a battery as well as a dynamo?

Get this

- Generators are used to make electricity.
- A source of energy is used to turn a turbine which turns a magnet in the generator.
- This induces a voltage across a coil, making electricity.

121

Learn about
- Energy conservation
- Sankey diagrams

Conservation of energy

You cannot create or destroy energy. We often say that it is lost but really it has been transferred to another form of energy that we don't want. The total amount of energy stays the same. This is the law of **conservation** of energy.

You want your television to change electrical energy to sound and light energy. But some of the electrical energy is transferred to heat energy. Your television gets warm. This is wasted energy.

 1   Draw an energy transfer diagram for the television.

Every time energy is transferred some is wasted. Equipment is always designed to keep the amount of wasted energy as small as possible. This saves money as well as valuable energy resources.

Generating electricity

Vast amounts of energy are transferred to electrical energy to supply everyone's needs. We use:

- fossil fuels
- solar power
- wind power
- hydro-electric power (HEP).

Each method wastes some energy.

This energy transfer diagram for a hydro-electric power station shows the main energy transfers that take place.

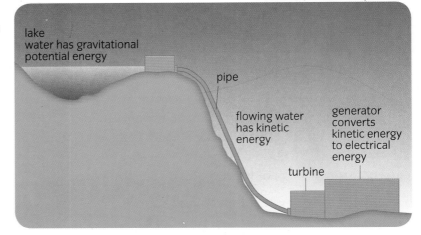

lake
water has gravitational potential energy

pipe

flowing water has kinetic energy

generator converts kinetic energy to electrical energy

turbine

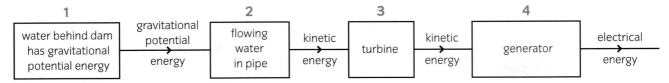

1		2		3		4	
water behind dam has gravitational potential energy	gravitational potential energy →	flowing water in pipe	kinetic energy →	turbine	kinetic energy →	generator	electrical energy →

At each stage energy is wasted. At stages **1** and **2** energy is wasted as heat due to **friction** between the water particles as they flow down towards the turbine. Energy is also wasted as sound.

 2   Why is energy wasted at stage 3?

3   How does the generator waste energy?

Sankey diagrams

Sankey diagrams summarise all the energy transfers taking place in a system. The thicker the arrow the greater the amount of energy involved. This Sankey diagram shows the energy transfers involved in a wind turbine.

About half of the wind energy moving towards the blades is transferred to kinetic energy of the blades.

 4 How does the Sankey diagram show that the electrical generator does not waste a lot of energy?

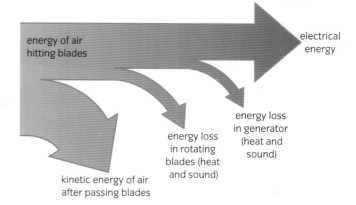

Drawing Sankey diagrams to scale

Sankey diagrams are often drawn to scale so that the width of the arrows represents the amount of each energy, in **joules** (J).

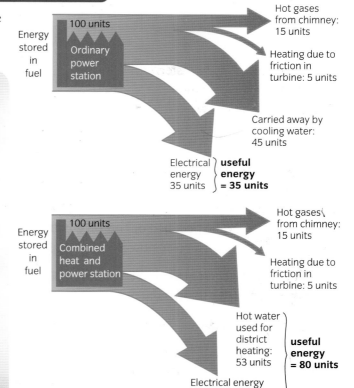

A typical **coal-fired power station** converts 3000 J of chemical energy from coal into about 1000 J of electrical energy. The rest is mainly lost as heat. So it is a heat generator rather than an electricity generator.

Energy is lost to the environment as heat at each stage. The dense (white) clouds are not smoke but steam coming from the cooling towers.

 5 What happens to the heat energy of this steam?

6 What proportion of the chemical energy stored in the coal is transferred to electrical energy?

Some power stations now use most of this wasted heat to heat nearby houses and factories. These 'combined heat and power (CHP) stations' only waste about a fifth of the input energy.

Summing up

7 Write down two disadvantages of burning coal in a power station to produce electricity.

8 In a power station, how much electrical energy is produced with an input of 1,000 J if 600 J is wasted?

9 10 000 J of electrical energy is needed to boil water in an electric kettle. 200 J is wasted. Draw a Sankey diagram for the kettle.

10 Suggest why the kettle wastes very little energy.

Get this

- You cannot create or destroy energy, only transfer it.
- All systems waste energy, usually as heat.
- Sankey diagrams summarise all the energy transfers taking place in a system.

Every little bit helps

The energy problem

More people worldwide want more electricity. Most electricity is still generated using non-renewable fossil fuels. But supplies of these are limited and burning them adds to global warming.

To solve this problem we need to find new renewable ways of providing electricity. Some of these are small scale but can make a big difference if enough people use them.

Solar power

A new type of solar panel has been invented that allows light to pass through it like a pane of glass. It is 10 times more powerful than existing methods of producing energy from sunlight. The glass in a window is painted with a transparent, organic dye to absorb light. It takes the light to photocells in the window frame, which convert it to electricity.

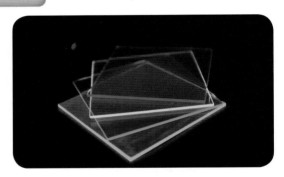

 1 Suggest one advantage of this type of solar panel.

Solar-powered rickshaws are now found on the streets of India. They can be pedalled or run off a battery that is recharged daily from a solar-powered charging station.

These rickshaws can reach a speed of about 20 metres per second, much faster than pedal power. As well as improving life for rickshaw drivers they have zero carbon footprint.

 2 Why is a battery needed rather than using the Sun's energy directly?

People power

Merry-go-rounds at rural schools in Ghana use some of the children's energy to generate electricity so the schools and villages can have some light. The children playing on a merry-go-round charge batteries.

 3 Explain how the merry-go-round makes electricity.

Electric cars

Traditional cars use oil, a fossil fuel, and so are a big source of pollution. **Electric cars** avoid this by running on batteries recharged from the mains electricity supply. Their top speeds are lower than those of ordinary cars and they need frequent recharging.

This bamboo electric car from Japan goes further – it can be put on a compost heap when it comes to the end of its useful life.

 4 Where are electric cars likely to be most useful?

More popular are 'hybrid' cars which use both petrol and electricity. They go faster and travel further than electric cars. Many governments are encouraging the use of both electric and hybrid cars.

 5 Give an advantage of a hybrid car over an electric one.

6 Give a disadvantage of a hybrid car over an electric one.

The drawback of both electric and hybrid cars, however, is that they both need electricity. If this is generated using fossil fuels it produces more greenhouse gases.

All cars have a battery which starts the engine. This is recharged when the engine is running. Some manufacturers have now invented a braking system which also tops up the battery when a car brakes.

Others recycle the heat energy from braking for use within the engine.

Hydrogen cars

New technology uses hydrogen to provide a source of energy for cars without producing any pollution. The only gas they produce is water vapour. Some **hydrogen cars** use liquid hydrogen in a conventional engine that can also run on petrol. Others, like this one, use **fuel cells** to make electricity. Fuel cells produce electricity by combining hydrogen with oxygen.

One of the biggest obstacles standing in the way of sales of fuel-cell cars is the lack of hydrogen fuelling stations.

 7 Why are sales of hydrogen cars unlikely to increase rapidly in the near future?

Summing up

8 Why are new methods of energy production focusing on renewable sources?

9 Draw an energy transfer diagram for a merry-go-round producing electricity.

10 Why may an electric car still cause pollution?

11 Give an advantage of hydrogen cars.

Get this

- The world needs to make more electricity without using more fossil fuels.
- Many new technologies, small and large, are being developed to do this.

125

The best energy source?

Demand for electricity

Most of the electricity in the UK, and the world, is generated using fossil fuels such as gas, oil and coal.

But they will run out, and burning them adds to greenhouse gases and global warming. Many people now believe that we need cleaner, and renewable ways of generating electricity. There is increasing protest against using coal, which produces more carbon dioxide than other fossil fuels.

 1 Look at the pie chart. How much of our electricity in 2007 was generated using fossil fuels?

2 How much electricity came from renewable sources?

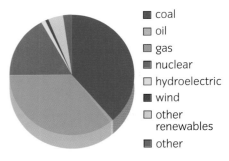

- coal
- oil
- gas
- nuclear
- hydroelectric
- wind
- other renewables
- other

▲ UK energy sources in 2007

Using fossil fuels

Drax in Yorkshire is the biggest coal-fired power station in Europe, more than twice as big as any other power station in the UK. It opened in the mid-1970s and it supplies enough electricity for about 1.5 million homes. It produces electricity night and day.

But Drax also produces huge amounts of carbon dioxide. Every year it produces about a quarter of the carbon dioxide emitted by all the cars in the UK.

Drax has now developed a system that burns a mixture of biomass and coal. Biomass is fuel made from waste plant and animal material as well as crops specially grown to provide fuel.

Drax will be able to burn more than 2.5 million tonnes of biomass a year. Biomass is renewable and cleaner but still produces greenhouse gases.

▲ Biomass at Drax

3 Why does burning biomass produce greenhouse gases?

Wind power

So can we replace burning fuel as a way of making electricity?

The UK has targets for replacing fossil fuels with cleaner and renewable energy sources. **Wind farms** on land and at sea are the most likely to help us meet these targets and provide most of our electricity for many years to come.

Suitable sites on land are limited. Wind farms take up a lot of space. Many people think they are noisy and unsightly. The wind does not always blow. The energy obtained varies with the speed of the wind.

4 Why are suitable sites for wind farms on land limited?

We need about 2000 very large wind turbines to provide as much power as one traditional power station. This is enough for about 600 000 homes. Several large-scale developments in the sea near the coast (off-shore) are now planned.

 5 Why are off-shore sites a good idea?

6 Give one problem of off-shore sites.

Wave power

The UK also has a lot of water around its huge coastline. A machine called the Searaser uses **wave power** to push water uphill to a reservoir on the cliffs above.

The upper float moves up and down with the waves. This movement forces water through the pipes up the cliff to the reservoir. It can then rush down to drive a hydroelectric generator.

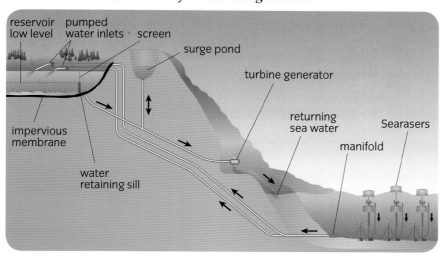

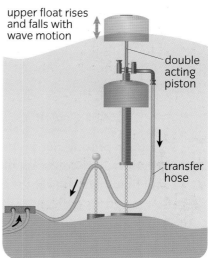

upper float rises and falls with wave motion

double acting piston

transfer hose

It is planned to build lots of these, maybe hundreds, side by side along the coast of the UK. One Searaser will provide enough energy for about 500 homes.

Summing up

7 Why is it important to look for new ways of generating electricity?

8 Crops are specially grown to provide biomass. Give one problem that this could cause.

9 List the advantages and disadvantages of wind power.

10 Biomass is a renewable fuel but not a 'clean' one. Explain why.

10 How many Searasers would be needed to supply 2 million homes?

11 Why is the UK a good place for Searasers?

Get this

- Fossils fuels are running out.
- All fuel burning makes greenhouse gases.
- Wind and wave power could generate much UK electricity in the future.

Learn about
- Saving energy
- Making electricity locally

Keeping it local

The world demand for electricity is growing all the time. Even using both fossil fuels and renewable energy sources it will be difficult to keep up. And if we want to reduce fossil fuel burning because of harmful greenhouse gases the problem is even greater.

So we also need to use less electricity. and perhaps make more of our own locally.

 1 Look at the photo of the city at night. How do you think energy is being wasted here?

Making it and saving it

The 800 pupils of Ringmer Community College in East Sussex are actively involved in protecting the environment. They have been so successful that they won the 2008 UK Secondary Schools section of the Ashden Awards for sustainable energy.

The school generates some of its electricity from a 2.5 kW wind turbine and a 7.5 kW array of solar cells on the roof of a teaching block.

They sell spare electricity to a national power company. They also cut down on wastage of electricity in school. In total they save about £6700 on electricity each year.

2 Suggest two ways in which less electricity may be wasted.

About 200 pupils are Eco-Reps:

- They monitor energy use and waste in the school. If school departments leave equipment and lights switched on or classroom doors open the Eco-Reps 'name and shame' them and can even fine them!
- They help to control the heating system, switching it off when it is not needed in the day. This saves £6000 a year on gas bills.

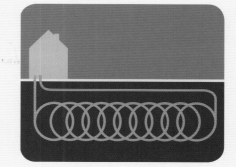

- They have helped to design a new sixth-form building. It is heated by a ground source **heat pump**. This uses a loop of piping buried in the ground filled with a mixture of water and antifreeze which is pumped around the pipe. The water absorbs heat from the ground and carries it back into the school.

 3 Why do the heat pump pipes contain antifreeze?

The money from the Ashden Award has been used to install screens around the school which show hour by hour how much electricity the school is generating and how much energy it is using. It has also been used to improve insulation in the main school building.

The school has installed biomass boilers which has reduced its carbon dioxide emissions.

 4 How will the screens and insulation help the pupils' energy saving campaign?

But beware, choose with care!

You need to choose the right type of renewable resource for your area to generate as much electricity as you can. Mr B fitted solar cells to the roof of his house in Scotland.

It cost £15 000. The saving on his electricity bill is about £150 a year. This means it will take him 100 years to get back the money he has spent.

We call this the **payback time**.   Payback time = $\dfrac{\text{cost of installation}}{\text{saving each year}}$

Ms C put a wind turbine on the roof of her house in Central London. It cost £3000. The saving on her electricity bill is about £50 a year.

5 Calculate Ms C's payback time.

6 Do you think Mr B and Ms C made wise choices? Explain.

Summing up

7 Why is the world demand for electricity increasing rapidly?

8 What renewable resources of electricity would be most suitable for your school?

9 Heat pumps have a payback time of 10 years. What does this mean?

10 How does the payback time for a heat pump compare with the payback time for wind turbines and solar panels?

Get this

- Electricity use is increasing.
- Suitable local renewable resources can help provide it
- But we need to save energy as well.

Learn about
- Average speed
- Distance–time graphs

Sailing

Dame Ellen MacArthur sailed into the record books in February 2001 at the age of 24 by becoming the youngest person and fastest woman to sail around the world alone.

In 2005 she gained the non-stop, round-the-world record, sailing more than 27 000 miles (43 200 kilometres) in just under 72 days (1728 hours).

Her speed varied all the time. In good sailing weather she went faster than when the boat was hit by huge storms or stuck for days with very little wind.

But we can say what **speed** she did on **average** over the whole journey by dividing the whole distance by the total time it took. This average speed makes it easier to compare how fast different people, or boats, or cars travel.

$$Average\ speed = \frac{total\ distance}{total\ time}$$

Science uses metric units so speed is measured in centimetres per second (cm/s), metres per second (m/s) or kilometres per hour (km/h). Ellen sailed 43 200 km in 1728 hours.

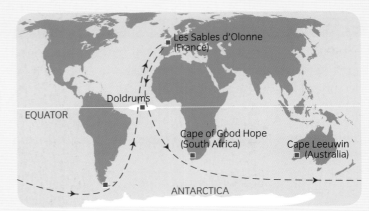

? 1 Calculate Ellen's average speed for the journey in km/h.

2 Was Ellen's maximum speed during the journey greater or smaller than her average speed? Explain your answer.

Ready, steady, SLOW!

In snail racing the snails start in the centre of a circle of radius 33 centimetres.

They are pointed towards the circumference 30 centimetres away. The first snail to reach the circumference is the winner.

We can show the progress of the snails on a graph like this one. We call this a **distance–time** graph as it shows the time taken to travel any distance within the journey.

The distance from the start of each snail was measured every 20 seconds. The steeper the line on the graph the faster the snail is moving.

3 Who won the race?

4 What was the winning time?

5 What was the average speed of each snail?

6 What was Harold doing at A?

7 Who was moving fastest as they crossed the finishing line?

8 Why don't we draw a straight line between each pair of points in this type of graph?

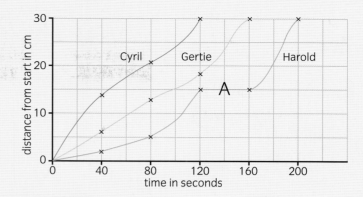

Comparing fairly

Time 10 seconds on your watch or stop-clock. In just under that time top sprinters like Jamaican Usain Bolt (see page 134) can run 100 metres! This is an average speed of more than 10 metres per second.

How can you compare the speeds of the snails, Ellen MacArthur and Usain Bolt? The answer is to turn them all into the same units. The standard unit of speed scientists use is metres per second (m/s).

- There are 1000 metres in 1 kilometre so you multiply a distance in kilometres by 1000 to convert it to metres.
- There are 100 centimetres in 1 metre so you divide a distance in centimetres by 100 to convert it to metres.

9 How do you convert hours to seconds?

10 Convert Ellen MacArthur's average speed on her round-the-world trip from km/h to m/s (see question 1).

11 Write down the average speeds of Usain, Ellen and the winning snail in m/s in increasing order.

Summing up

12 On Sports Day Alfie ran the 100 m race in 19 seconds and Jake in 15 seconds. Who ran faster?

13 Ellen MacArthur won a transatlantic solo race, the Route du Rhum. She sailed 6350 km in 13.5 days. Calculate her average speed in km/h.

14 The distance between the start and finish points in the Route du Rhum race is 5680 km. Suggest why Ellen sailed further than this.

15 A racing cyclist completed a race in 250 s at an average speed of 16 m/s. How long, in metres, was the race?

Get this

- Average speed = $\dfrac{\text{total distance}}{\text{total time}}$
- In science speed is usually measured in m/s.
- A distance–time graph shows how distance changes with time.

Formula 1 racing

Formula 1 cars are designed to reach speeds far greater than ordinary cars.

Lewis Hamilton won the 2008 Grand Prix race in China covering 305 kilometres in just over one and a half hours.

Learn about
- Presenting data
- Analysing data
- Drawing graphs

? **1** Calculate Hamilton's average speed for the 2008 China Grand Prix in km/h.

There are 18 races in the World Championship. The table shows the number of races won by each winning driver in 2008.

This table arranges the data alphabetically by surname. We could also show it in a diagram such as a pie chart or pictogram or **histogram** (bar chart).

The pie chart is divided into 18 equal parts, each one representing a race. A pie chart is circular so it has 360° at the centre. So the slice for each race is 360° divided by 18, that is 20°.

Winning driver		Number of races won
Fernando Alonso	(FA)	2
Lewis Hamilton	(LH)	5
Heikki Kovalainen	(HK)	1
Robert Kubica	(RK)	1
Felipe Massa	(FM)	6
Kimi Räikkönen	(KR)	2
Sebastian Vettel	(SV)	1

? **2** How many degrees represent the slice of pie for Felipe Massa?

3 Which method do you think is clearest? Explain why.

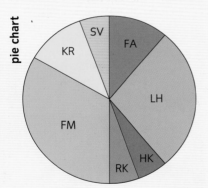

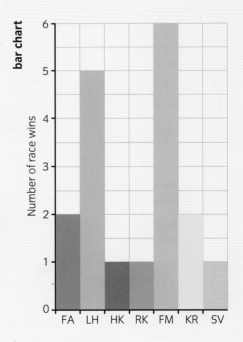

Drawing line graphs

Line graphs are a good way of showing information when you want to link two sets of numbers, both of which are changing continually. We call these **continuous variables**.

? **4** Why couldn't we show the data about F1 winners using a line graph?

For example, the speed of one racing car over a race varies all the time as it goes round the track. Sometimes it increases speed, **accelerates**. Sometimes it decreases speed, **decelerates**. You can use a line graph to show this more clearly.

The table shows the speed of a racing car during the first twenty seconds of a race. If this data is shown as a **speed–time** graph it gives us a better idea of how speed is continually changing during the race.

- When the line rises the car is accelerating.
- When the line goes downwards the car is decelerating.
- When the line is flat the car's speed is constant.

Time in s	Speed in km/h
0	0
2	100
4	195
6	270
8	310
10	320
12	320
14	320
16	300
18	280
20	300

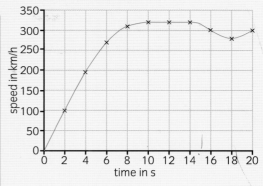

5 Between which times was the speed **constant**?

6 Between which times was the car decelerating?

7 Between which times was the car accelerating?

We could also draw a distance–time graph for the racing car like the one for the snail race on page 131. This shows the distance the car has travelled from the start at times up to 20 seconds.

Readings were taken every 2 seconds but the distance was changing all the time. This is why we always join points with a smooth curve.

Time in s	Distance in m
0	0
2	28
4	80
6	170
8	330
10	510
12	680
14	860
16	1030
18	1200
20	1360

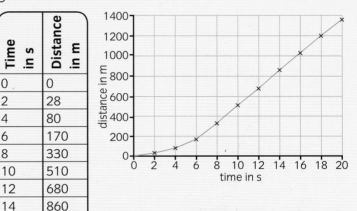

8 How far did the car travel in the first 9 seconds?

9 Why isn't the distance–time graph horizontal between 10 and 14 seconds, like the speed–time graph?

10 Why does the line on this graph never go downwards?

Summing up

11 Hamilton won the 2008 Grand Prix at Silverstone, covering 308 km in 1 hour 19 minutes (1·32 h). Calculate his average speed in km/h.

12 Use the speed–time graph to estimate the speed of the racing car after 15 seconds.

13 Use the distance–time graph to estimate the distance the racing car travelled in the first 15 seconds of the race.

14 During the race the car stops in the pits for 10 seconds. How would this be represented on the line of the distance–time graph? How would this be represented on the line of the speed–time graph?

Get this

- Data can be compared in various forms such as pie charts, pictograms and bar graphs.
- Line graphs show how continuous variables may be linked.
- Distance–time graphs show distance travelled over time.
- Speed–time graphs show how speed changes over time.

Precision and accuracy

Usain Bolt won Olympic gold in 2008 by running 100 m in a record time of 9.69 seconds – and he started to celebrate 20 m from the finish. But the world's second fastest man in 2008, Asafa Powell, ran it in 9.72 seconds. When differences are so small, athletes have to be timed as *accurately* and *precisely* as possible.

Precision is shown by the number of decimal places given for the time. Without 2 decimal places it would be impossible to say whether Usain Bolt or Asafa Powell held the world record in 2008. Both are 9.7 seconds to one decimal place.

If no decimal places were used all the athletes' times in this race would be rounded to 10 seconds as they are all in the **range** 9.5 to 10.5 seconds. Again this is not much use!

1 How much faster was Usain Bolt's time compared to Asafa Powell's?

Accuracy tells you how correct a measurement is. A measurement can be very precise but still not be accurate. If Usain Bolt's time had been recorded as 9.79 seconds it would have the same precision but be very inaccurate.

Timing methods

School Sports Day races are still timed using a stopwatch, although it is now a digital one. But it is not the stopwatch that limits the accuracy of the timing. It takes time for the timekeeper to react to
- seeing the smoke from the starting gun to start the stopwatch
- seeing the winner cross the line to stop it.

This is called **reaction time**. It is the time the brain takes to process the information. It is different for everyone but is usually about 0.7 seconds. This is large when timing a race that only lasts for 10 seconds or so.

In top class races today the starter's gun triggers the timing clock. At the end of the race the winning athlete runs through a light beam. An optical device senses that the light beam has been cut and stops the clock.

2 Why is an automatic timing system better than using people with accurate, precise stop clocks?

3 Suggest why sprinters bend forward at the finish line.

False starts

The shorter the race the more important it is to detect a false start. A 100 metre race takes about 10 seconds. If a runner 'jumps the gun' by only 0.1 second they travel about one metre in that time.

Each set of starting blocks has a loudspeaker linked to the starter's pistol so that all competitors hear the start signal at precisely the same time.

There are built-in **sensors** in the starting blocks. The system measures each runner's reaction time. This is the time between the sound of the starter's pistol and the change in pressure of their foot against the block. If it is less than the time in which they can possibly react to the sound of the starter's gun, the timekeeper signals a false start.

 4 Explain why there would be a problem if each set of starting blocks did not have its own loudspeaker.

Summing up

5 Why is automatic timing more important for a sprint race than a marathon?

6 Sam and Ella time an 800 metre race at their school Sports Day. Sam records the time as 2 minutes 21.4 seconds. Ella records it as 2 minutes 21 seconds. Whose reading is more precise? Whose reading is more accurate?

7 In swimming races there are sensors in the starting blocks at the start of the race and touch pad sensors attached to the side of the pool at each end. Suggest how a freestyle race is timed.

Get this

- Accuracy is how close a measurement is to its true value.
- Precision is the number of decimal places to which a value is given.
- Reaction time is the time the brain takes to process information.

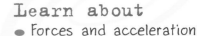

Getting moving

Sprinters need to increase their speed very quickly at the start of a race. To get this acceleration they need a big forward **force**. A force is always needed to get things moving. The greater the forward force the greater the acceleration.

Sprinters start from a crouching position. This means that more of the force from their legs is in the horizontal direction forwards – the way they want to go. So they get a good forward acceleration.

Sprinters often use starting blocks like the ones in the picture. They push back on the blocks. The blocks push against their feet. This extra pushing force helps them accelerate rapidly.

▲ get set.....

▲ ....go!

? 1 Why don't distance runners use starting blocks?

Slowing down

A backwards force is needed to make things slow down. The greater the backward force the greater the deceleration.

Racing bikes need good brakes to slow down quickly as they enter a corner. They also need to accelerate rapidly as they turn out of it. These rapid changes require big forces.

Several forces act on moving objects and slow them down; for example:
- friction with the ground
- **air resistance** or **drag**

? 2 Look at the bikers in the photograph. What features keep the backward forces as small as possible?

When the forces on a moving object are **balanced** it moves at a constant speed. When the forces on a moving object are **unbalanced** it accelerates or decelerates.

In the diagrams the length of each force arrow shows the size of the force – the longer it is the greater the force. The blue arrow shows the direction in which the object is moving.

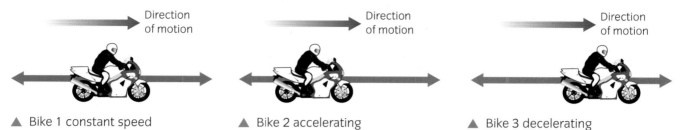

Direction of motion

Direction of motion

Direction of motion

▲ Bike 1 constant speed

▲ Bike 2 accelerating

▲ Bike 3 decelerating

 3 What would happen to bike 1 if the force to the right increased?

4 What change must be made for bike 2 to have a constant speed?

Calculating forces

If you have a *stationary* object being pulled to the right by a force of 6 newtons (N) and to the left by a force of 2 N, it will start to move to the right with a force of 4 N. We call the 4 N to the right the **resultant force**. (You can think of it as the result of taking one force away from the other.)

 2N ← ● → 6N

 2N ← ● → 10N

 2N ← ● → 2N

▲ The resultant force is 4 N to the right. It accelerates to the right.

▲ The resultant force is 8 N to the right. It has a greater acceleration to the right.

▲ The resultant force is zero. It will not move at all.

If an object is already *moving* its motion *changes* when there is a resultant force.

- If the resultant force is forwards it will accelerate.
- If the resultant force is backwards it will decelerate.
- If the resultant force is zero it travels at a constant speed.

 5 What is happening to a moving vehicle if the forces on it are balanced?

Summing up

6 Ruby is driving her car at a constant speed. What can you say about the forces acting on it?

7 What must happen to these forces if Ruby approaches traffic lights at red?

8 Describe the motion of a stationary model car when a 20 N force to the left and a 12 N force to the right act on it.

9 Spacecraft are shot into space by rockets but when the rockets stop firing the spacecraft carry on moving. Why?

Get this

- Balanced forces on an object mean that it is not moving or is moving at a constant speed.
- Unbalanced forces mean that it is accelerating or decelerating.
- The change in an object's motion depends on the resultant force acting on it.

137

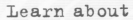

Learn about
- The effects of drag
- Reducing drag

British cyclists strike gold

Rebecca Romero was one of the British cycling gold medallists at the 2008 Beijing Olympics. The team collected eight gold medals between them, compared to two in the 2004 Olympics.

But the team had to return their cycling suits after the Olympic Games and they were shredded! Why?

The British team think the suit is crucial to their success. It is a closely guarded secret and the performance director of British Cycling wants to keep it that way until after the London Games in 2012.

The suit is a super-**aerodynamic** 'skinsuit'. It was designed to reduce drag from the air. Drag is a frictional force on moving objects in air (or a liquid) which reduces their speed. The suit makes the air move more smoothly and quickly over the surface of the body and reduces the drag force. This is called **streamlining**.

1 What happens to the speed of a cyclist if drag is reduced?

2 Name a sport that needs to reduce drag in a liquid.

More secrets of success

Cycling technology has been developing for some time. In 1992 a British cyclist, Chris Boardman, won gold on one of the first racing bikes made from low-density carbon fibre. This is much lighter than metal and the frame is moulded in one piece.

For the 2004 Olympics, new cycle helmets were designed for the British team to reduce drag. This picture shows some of the computer modelling done on how design might reduce drag.

3 How do lighter bicycle frames help increase speed?

4 How can bicycle helmets help reduce drag?

Since 2004, the British cycling team have also had an intensive training programme shaped to the individual needs of each athlete. They have also been supported by a whole team of scientists working to improve cycling technology. Cycles, cyclists and their clothing are tested in wind tunnels to find out how aerodynamic they are. The smoother the flow of air, the less drag there is on the cyclist.

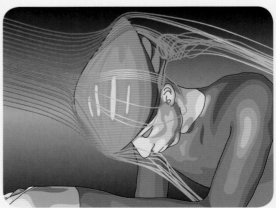

5 The picture on the left opposite shows a modern racing cyclist in a wind tunnel, the one on the right shows competitors in the 1972 Olympics. How is the modern cyclist more streamlined?

Making a difference?

Can changes in technology really have that much effect on the chances of winning? This table shows winning times for the men's 4000 metre pursuit event in Olympics since 1968, in minutes and seconds (eg 4:22.44 is 4 minutes and 22.44 seconds).

1968	1972	1976	1980	1984	1988	1992	1996	2000	2004	2008
4:22.44	4:22.14	4:21.06	4:15.70	4:25.99	4:13.31	4:08.79	4:05.93	3:59.71	3:58.23	3:53.31

6 Draw a graph or chart which presents this data so that you can see the patterns in it clearly.

7 Does this provide evidence that changes in cycling technology since 1990 have improved times? What other factors might be involved?

This table shows the performance of the cycling pursuit teams over the 2000, 2004 and 2008 Olympic Games (*best* times of medallists throughout the competition):

	2000	2004	2008
Gold	Germany 3:59.71	Australia 3:58.23	Great Britain 3:53.31
Silver	Ukraine 4:04.52	Great Britain 4:01.76	Denmark 3:56.83
Bronze	Great Britain 4:01.98	Spain 4:05.52	New Zealand 3:57.78

8 Does this data suggest that the British team is right to believe that the new technology it has developed since 2000 has been important in its success?

Summing up

9 Do you think there is a limit to how much the drag can be reduced? Explain.

10 What other factors contribute to record times?

11 Explain how swimmers reduce the drag force acting on them.

Get this

- Drag is a frictional force on objects moving through air or a liquid.
- Drag reduces the speed at which things can travel.
- Drag can be reduced if the surfaces are smoother.
- Drag can be reduced if a shape is streamlined.

How fast can you go?

Beating drag

You have seen how more streamlined shapes for cyclists cut down drag, which is a frictional force backwards on the cyclist.

For a racing cyclist the drag is mainly air resistance. The cyclist and bike have to push air molecules out of the way to go forward. Top cyclists like Chris Hoy complete a 200 metre sprint race in less than 20 seconds.

1 Estimate his average speed.

2 Why does crouching over the handlebars reduce air resistance?

3 What could the street cyclist do to go faster?

In the team pursuit event the team members use other ways of reducing the effect of air resistance on their speed. Two opposing four-person teams race over 4000 metres. Each rider takes it in turn to lead for half a lap and then moves to the back. The lead cyclists have to work much harder as air resistance is much greater on them. The other cyclists have an easier ride until it is their turn to lead again.

With the best teams there is only a few centimetres between the wheels. So a high-speed pile-up is only a tiny lapse in concentration away!

4 Estimate their average speed.

▲ The Great Britain pursuit team won the gold medal in the 2008 Olympics in a world record time of 3 m 53.314 s (3:53.314).

This is faster than the average speed of Chris Hoy – and they need the stamina to complete 4000 metres! This shows the advantage gained by sharing the lead position.

5 What does this tell you about the size of the air resistance on high-speed cyclists?

Speed and velocity

We often use speed and **velocity** to mean the same but this is not quite true. Speed means how fast something moves; eg 20 m/s. Velocity means how fast and in what direction something moves, eg 20 m/s due north.

Emily and Anya are swimming a 50 metre race. The pool is 25 metres long. They start and finish at the right hand end of the pool. At the instant shown they both have a speed of 2 m/s. Anya's velocity is 2 m/s to the right.

6 What is Emily's velocity?

7 Who is in the lead?

Maximum speed

Cyclists' speed varies throughout a race. When a maximum speed is reached the forces on them are balanced. The forward force of the cyclist pedalling is equal to the drag force backwards. They are travelling at a constant speed and cannot go any faster. This is called their **terminal velocity**.

To make it even harder, air resistance increases as speed increases. When going slowly the drag is small. As the speed increases more air molecules have to be pushed out of the way each second so the drag increases.

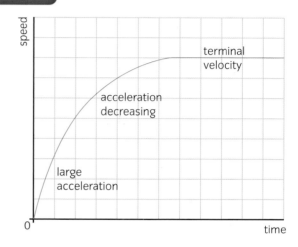

▲ cyclist moving slowly so drag is small

▲ moving faster so drag is bigger

▲ forces balanced – terminal velocity

Racing cyclists aim to keep the backward force as small as possible. This means they can go faster before the forces acting balance, which gives them a greater top speed.

Summing up

8 What can you say about the forces acting on an object moving at terminal velocity?

9 What can an athlete running in a 100 m race do to be streamlined?

10 Sam walks 2 km south at 3 km/h and then 1 km east at 3 km/h. Explain why her velocity is not constant. How long does she take?

11 Why do free-fall parachutists try to make the air resistance as big as possible while cyclists try to reduce it?

Get this

- Terminal velocity is the maximum constant speed reached by a moving object.
- It occurs when the forces on the object are balanced.
- Velocity means speed in a certain direction.

Jumping up and down

Trampolining

At Olympic level, trampolining is like top class gymnastics with extra bounce. But everyone can have fun on a trampoline without this level of skill.

As Ellie lands on her trampoline the **springs** stretch. The stretching force in the springs, called the **tension**, increases. This extra tension means there is an unbalanced force on Ellie which pushes her up in the air again.

Ellie's 15-year old brother, Tom, weighs much more than Ellie. When he bounces on the trampoline the springs stretch more. Is there a relationship between weight and the amount the springs stretch?

Stretching springs

Ellie's trampoline has a weight limit of 1200 N. Tom decides to find out why.

He measures the **extension** of a spring when pulled by bigger and bigger forces. His results are shown in the table.

Tom plots his results onto a **line graph**. He draws a line of best fit. This is a smooth line that travels through or very close to as many of the points plotted as possible.

Pulling force in N	Extension in cm
0	0
2	1.1
4	2.0
6	2.5
8	4.2
10	5.4
12	6.8
14	8.5
16	11.0

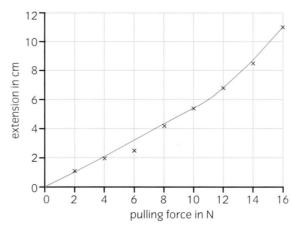

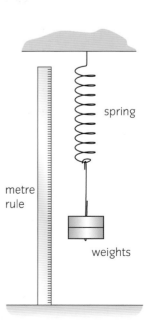

Tom's line was straight at first but then curved. One point was far away from the line. We call this an **anomalous point**, or **outlier**. Tom probably measured the extension wrongly. By drawing a graph he can easily see it is wrong and ignore or repeat the reading. All the other points are close to the best-fit line.

 1 Write down the pulling force for the anomalous point.

2 Do you think Tom's results are accurate? Explain.

3 Do you think Tom's results are precise? Explain.

What does the graph show?

The straight line through the origin shows that the pulling force is proportional to the extension. This means that when the pulling force doubles, the extension also doubles. This is no longer true when the line curves.

 4 Over what range of pulling forces is the graph a straight line?

5 What happens to the extension when the graph curves?

When Tom removed the weights afterwards he found that the spring was longer than at the start. He repeated the investigation with a new spring but this time he took the weights off between each reading and measured the length of the spring after it had bounced back.

He found that up to 10 N it returned to its original length. After that it stayed stretched. It was **permanently extended**. This was when the graph line curved. Tom had exceeded the spring's elastic limit. Beyond this point it will never return to its original length.

If too many people jumped on the trampoline at once the springs could exceed their elastic limit.

 6 Explain why trampolines have a weight limit.

Compression

The gymnast vaults over a box. She takes off from a springboard for extra upward push.

The five springs are **compressed**, or squashed, when she jumps on it. The amount of compression is proportional to the force on the springs.

Summing up

7 What is meant by the '**elastic limit**' of a spring?

8 How would the graph Tom plotted change if he used a stronger spring?

9 If a boy weighing 600 N used the springboard above, what would be the force on each spring?

Get this

- Springs have a tension force in them when stretched.
- The extension in a spring is proportional to the pulling force, if the spring does not pass its elastic limit.
- The bigger the pushing force the more a spring is compressed.

Learn about
- Acceleration
- Interpreting line graphs

Speeding up and slowing down

F1 racing cars accelerate very rapidly at the start of a race. The more quickly the speed increases the greater the acceleration.

A Formula 1 car can accelerate and then decelerate from 0 mph to 100 mph to 0 mph in 6 seconds! Accelerating from 0 to 100 mph (160 km/h) takes about 3.6 seconds.

 1 How long does it take to go from 100 to 0 mph?

This speed–time graph shows how the speed of a car changes as it starts to move.

 2 Is the car accelerating, decelerating or moving at a constant speed?

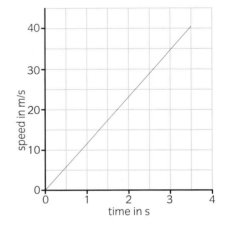

When a car is decelerating its speed is decreasing. The more quickly the speed decreases the greater the deceleration.

Calculating acceleration

To find the acceleration of a car over a certain time period
- take its speed at the start away from its final speed to find how much the speed has increased
- divide the increase in speed by the time

$$\text{Acceleration} = \frac{\text{increase in speed}}{\text{time}} \text{ or } \frac{[\text{final speed} - \text{starting speed}]}{\text{time}}$$

Acceleration is measured in m/s^2. If a car accelerates from 0 to 30 m/s in 6 seconds its acceleration is $\frac{[30-0]}{6} = 5 m/s^2$.

If the final speed is smaller than the starting speed the car slows down. The acceleration is negative. This is deceleration. If a car decelerates from 30 m/s to 20 m/s in 5 s its acceleration is $\frac{[20-30]}{5} = -2 m/s^2$. We say it has a *deceleration* of $2 m/s^2$.

 3 A train accelerates from 10 m/s to 12 m/s in 10 s. Calculate its acceleration.

4 Calculate the acceleration of the Formula 1 car above in m/s^2. (Look back at page 131 if you have forgotten how to change km/h to m/s.)

The Bugatti Veyron, one of the fastest cars on the road, accelerates from 0 to 100 km/h in just 3 seconds. It has a top speed of 406 km/h. This is a greater acceleration than a F1 car. But it can't beat F1 at higher speeds.

 5 Calculate the acceleration, in m/s², of the Bugatti.

Interpreting graph lines

The graph shows how the speeds of two cars changes as they start to move.

The speed of B changes more quickly than that of A. B has a bigger acceleration than A. The steeper the graph line the bigger the acceleration.

Look at the speed-time graph for car A again.

The graph line for car A is straight. It passes through the points (0,0), (1,12), (2,24), (3,36) etc.

The speed of car A increases by 12m/s every second. Its acceleration is **constant**.

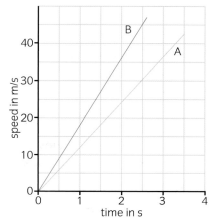

 6 Write down the acceleration of car A.

Force and acceleration

Look at the graph showing the acceleration of a model car for various resultant forces.

The graph is a straight line through the origin. This means the acceleration is **proportional** to the resultant force. If the resultant force doubles, the acceleration also doubles.

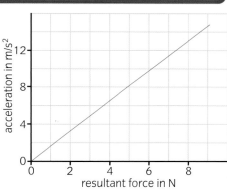

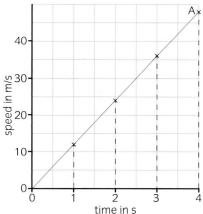

 7 What is the acceleration if the resultant force is 5N?

Summing up

8 Two car adverts claim '0 to 60 mph in 6 s!' and '0 to 80 mph in 10 seconds!' Which car has the greater acceleration?

9 A car accelerates from 10 m/s to 20 m/s in 5 seconds at a steady rate. Calculate its acceleration.

10 The Bugatti takes 14 seconds to reach 320 km/h from rest. Calculate its acceleration. Compare it with your answer to Q5.

11 A racing car brakes from 80 m/s to 50 m/s with a deceleration of 7.5 m/s². How long did it take?

Get this

- Acceleration = change in $\frac{\text{speed}}{\text{time}}$.
- Acceleration is measured in m/s².
- A straight line on a speed graph shows constant acceleration.
- A curved line shows changing acceleration.

145

Glossary

A

Accelerates: speeds up

Acceleration: the amount by which speed increases in one second

Accuracy: accurate: correct, without any mistakes

Aerobic respiration: respiration which uses oxygen to release energy from glucose and produces carbon dioxide and water vapour

Aerodynamic: object designed to reduce resistance to motion from the air (drag); streamlined

Air pressure: the force exerted by air particles when they collide with 1 metre squared (ms^2) of a surface

Air resistance : friction force on an object moving through the air causing it to slow down (also known as drag)

Alcohol: a compound made up of atoms of carbon, hydrogen and oxygen that is in alcoholic drinks

Alloy: a mixture of one or more other elements with a metal (usually other metals, except for carbon in steel)

Aluminium: a low density metal element

Alveoli: thin walled sacs in your lungs where oxygen diffuses into the blood and carbon dioxide diffuses out

Anaerobic respiration: respiration which releases energy from glucose without using oxygen – in humans this only happens for short periods in muscles and produces lactic acid

Anomalous point: point on a graph that does not fit the general pattern (also called an outlier)

Antagonistic (muscles): muscles that work in pairs by pulling bones in opposite directions

Antibiotic: a substance which destroys bacteria

Arteries: thick walled blood vessels which carry blood under high pressure away from the heart

Astronomer: scientist who studies space

Atmosphere: the layer of air above Earth's surface

Atmospheric pressure: force on an area of Earth's surface or the atmosphere due to the weight of air above it

Atom: smallest particle of an element which can exist

Average: value found by adding a set of values together and dividing by the number of values (also called the mean)

B

Bacteria: single celled microbes with a cell wall but no nucleus

Balanced forces: forces that are the same size but act in opposite directions on an object

Bar chart: a way of presenting data when only one variable is a number

Battery: two or more electrical cells joined together

Best-fit line: a smooth line on a graph that travels through or very close to as many of the points plotted as possible

Bioaccumulation: an increase in the concentration of chemicals such as pesticides moving along the food chain or from soil or water into plants

Biodegradable: a substance which can be broken down by natural processes of decay

Biodiesel: a biofuel made from plant oils

Biodiversity: the number and variety of different species in an area

Bioethanol: a biofuel made from carbohydrates like sugar

Biofuels: fuel produced from renewable resources

Biomass: the total mass of living material in an area

Blood vessel: tubes carrying blood around the body which may be arteries, veins or capillaries

C

Capillaries: the narrowest types of blood vessel

Carbohydrate: a nutrient providing energy

Carbon atoms: the tiny particles which make up the non-metal element carbon

Carbon cycle: this shows how carbon moves between the atmosphere, the sea, rocks, the soil and living things Carbon exists in different compounds in different parts of the carbon cycle

Carbon dioxide: gas found in small amounts in the atmosphere which plants use to make food and which contributes to global warming

Carbonate: the name of a group of chemicals which contain carbon and oxygen and make carbon dioxide when they react with acid (eg calcium carbonate)

Carnivore: a meat eating animal

Cartilage: tough elastic connective tissue found between bones at joints and in stiff structures like the windpipe

Cell: the building block living things are made from

Cell wall: tough outer covering of plant cells which helps to keep them rigid

Chlorine: a non-metal element At room temperature it is a green gas

Chloroplasts: the green parts of plant cells which capture light energy to make food from water and carbon dioxide

Cilia: tiny hair-like structures which sweep things along tubes in the body

Circulatory system: the organ system which transports substances to every tissue, consisting of the heart, blood vessels and blood

Classification: sorting things into groups according to their similarities and differences

Climate change: changes to long-term weather patterns as a result of global warming

Coal-fired power station: these burn the fossil fuel, coal, to generate electricity

Cochlea: a snail-shaped tube in the inner ear that houses the sensory cells that detect sound

Collaborate, collaboration: to work together with others on a project

Combustion: burning, when a substance reacts quickly with oxygen and gives out energy

Communicate: to share and exchange information

Competition: what happens when the supply of resources is limited and more than one organism tries to take them

Compounds: substance made of two or more elements chemically joined together

Compressed: squashed into a smaller space

Concentration: the amount of a substance that is dissolved in a certain volume of a solution

Conclude: to make a statement about what the results of an investigation tell you

Condense: turn from a gas into a liquid

Conservation (of energy): energy is never made or lost but is always transferred from one form to another

Constant: not changing

Contaminated: something that contains a toxic chemical

Continuous variables: a variable which can have any value across a range, eg time, temperature, length

Continuous variation: variation in a features that can take any value in a wide range, like height or weight

Contract: get smaller

Corrosion: the reaction of substances, usually metals, with air, and sometimes water as well

Creative thinking: thinking in a new way

Crude oil: a thick black liquid formed underground from the remains of prehistoric plants and animals that died millions of years ago It is used to make fuels, such as petrol and diesel, and many plastics

Crystal: a solid with its atoms arranged in a regular pattern, eg salt, diamond

Cytoplasm: the jelly-like substance inside a cell where most chemical reactions take place

D

Data: measurements taken from an investigation

Decelerates: slows down

Deceleration: the amount by which speed decreases in one second

Decibel: a unit of sound intensity or loudness

Decomposers: organisms that feed off dead plants or animals eg bacteria and fungi

Density: the mass of a substance in a certain volume

Diffuse: spread out from areas with many particles to areas with few eg from the small intestine to the blood and between the air and the blood during gas exchange in the lungs

Dissolves: when a solid mixes with a liquid to make a solution

Distance-time graph: shows how the distance travelled varies with time

Distillation: a way of separating a solvent from a solution (eg water from salty water) or liquids with different boiling points from a mixture

Dominant: a gene that controls the features a plant or animal develops, even when they also contain a different version of that gene

Donor: a person who donates a tissue or organ like blood

Drag: friction force on an object moving through air or water causing it to slow down

Dynamo: a device that transforms kinetic energy into electrical energy (a small generator)

E

Economic: related to cost

Elastic limit: the point beyond which a spring will never return to its original length when the pulling force is removed

Electric cars: cars powered by electric batteries

Electric current: flow of electric charge (electrons) around a complete circuit

Electrical energy: energy which makes current flow around a circuit and is changed in circuit components to other forms of energy (eg a light bulb changes it to light and heat energy)

Electromagnet: temporary magnet created using an electric current

Electromagnetic radiation: radiation with electric and magnetic properties that can travel through a vacuum (eg Sun's radiation)

Element: substance consisting of atoms of only one type

Embryo: a plant or animal which is just beginning to grow from a fertilised egg before it has all of its organs

Energy: needed to make things happen

Energy self sufficient: a community that produces enough energy to supply its needs using local resources

Engineer: a person who designs, builds or repairs machines, engines, or structures

Environmental: anything related to the environment

Environmental factors: something about a organism's environment that affects its growth or development eg the amount of light a plant receives

Environmental variation: variation influenced by environmental influences eg the language you speak

Enzyme: a substance made by living things that speeds up chemical reactions like the breakdown of large insoluble food molecules

Ethanol: a compound made up of atoms of carbon, hydrogen and oxygen which is the alcohol in alcoholic drinks

Evidence: observations and measurements which support or disprove a scientific theory

Extension: the amount an object gets longer

F

Features: the characteristics an individual has eg blue eyes

Fermentation: a reaction in which yeast produces ethanol and carbon dioxide from sugars

Fertile: able to produce offspring

Fertilised: an egg fused with a sperm

Fibreglass: a strong, light material made from a plastic strengthened with thin glass strands

Filter: a way of removing large pieces of solid from a mixture with liquids or smaller pieces of solid

Foam: a substance that has many gas bubbles trapped in a liquid or solid

Forces: act on objects and affect their movement, eg pushes, pulls, gravity, upthrust, friction

Formula (plural formulae): a way of showing the number of atoms of different elements in a compound using symbols and numbers, eg H_2O

Fossil fuels: fuels made from the decay of the remains of animals and plants which died millions of years ago, eg coal, oil, natural gas

Fraction: part of a liquid mixture which has liquids with different boiling points

Fractional distillation: heating a liquid mixture to separate it into fractions with different boiling points

Friction: a force that resists movement

Fuel cell: a device that uses chemical reactions to generate electricity

Fungi: a types of decomposer – many are microbes and are useful in making food and drink - others can cause infections like athlete's foot

G

Galaxy: a group of millions of stars

Generator: a device that transforms kinetic energy into electrical energy

Genes: the instructions inherited from your parents, which influence the way your body develops

Genetic engineering: a technique used to add extra genes to an organism

Genetically modified: a living thing which has had extra genes added to it from another organism

Glucose: a simple sugar used for respiration - formed when complex carbohydrates like starch are broken down in your digestive system

Gravitational fields: regions in which there is a force on a mass due to its attraction to other masses (eg things falling to the ground)

Gravitational potential energy: energy stored in an object because of its height above the ground

Gravity: the force of attraction between two objects because of their mass

Growth factor: a chemical signal that controls cell growth

H

Habitat: the place where a plant or animal lives

Hallucinogen: a drug which distorts your senses by causing chemical changes in your brain

Heat pump: a device that transfers heat from the ground to a building on the surface

Histogram: another name for a bar chart

Hormones: chemicals that are released into the blood stream to change the way specific organs or tissues work eg adrenalin

Hybrid: a plant or animal that is a cross between two species because its parents belong to different species

Hybrid car: a car that can run both on electricity from a battery or petrol in a petrol engine

Hydrocarbons: compounds made up of carbon and hydrogen only

Hydro-electric: a way of generating electricity using the energy of water falling downhill

Hydrogen: a non-metal element which exists as a gas at room temperature

I

Identical twins: twins formed when an early embryo splits into two identical groups of stem cells, which then develop into separate embryos

Imitation: when one individual copies something another individual does

Induced (voltage): voltage produced when a conductor is in a changing magnetic field

Infrared: a type of electromagnetic radiation which transfers heat energy from a hotter to a colder place

Inheritance: when genes are passed from a parent to their offspring

Inherited: passed on from a parent

Inherited variation: variation which results from different combinations of genes individuals inherit

Insoluble: a substance that does not dissolve in a solvent

Instinctive behaviour patterns: a pattern of behaviour inherited by all members of a species

Interdependent: living things which rely on each other for survival

Invertebrate: an animal without a backbone

Iron: a metal element that is the main substance in steel

Iron core: iron rod placed in a coil to increase the magnetic field strength when a current flows in the coil

J

Joints: places where bones meet

Joule: unit of energy

K

Kinetic energy: movement energy

L

Landfill: getting rid of waste by buying it

Lava: hot liquid rock which is on – or above – the surface of the Earth

Learned behaviours: behaviours that develop after an animal is born - animals repeat them to gain rewards or avoid negative consequences

Ligaments: the strong bands of tissue that link bones together

Light year: the distance light travels in one year

Limestone: a type of sedimentary rock made mainly from calcium carbonate

Line graph: a way of presenting results when there are two numerical variables

M

Magma: hot liquid rock which is underground

Magnetic field: area around a magnet where there is a force on a magnetic material

Mammal: a warm blooded vertebrate which feeds its young on milk like whales and humans

Marble: a metamorphic rock formed from limestone

Mars: a rocky planet fourth in order of the planets from the Sun

Mass: the amount of matter in something

Materials scientist: a scientist who studies the properties of materials such as metals and plastics

Membrane: the layer around the outside of a cell that controls what enters and leaves

Metals: a group of elements which are good conductors of heat and electricity

Metamorphic (rock): formed by the action of intense heat and pressure on sedimentary or igneous rock

Meteorite: a stony or metallic object that has fallen to Earth from outer space

Methane: a gas which is a type of hydrocarbon (containing carbon and hydrogen atoms)

Microbes: organisms which are too small to be seen without a microscope (microorganisms)

Microwaves: electromagnetic waves used for cooking and satellite communications

Minerals: chemicals like calcium, iron, potassium, phosphorous which are needed to keep the bodies of plants and animals healthy

Mitochondria: the compartments inside cells where aerobic respiration takes place

Mixture: containing two or more elements or compounds mixed together

Model: a simplified description of a process

Molecule: a particle of a substance made from two or more atoms that are strongly joined together

Moon: rocky body orbiting Earth; it is Earth's only natural satellite

Mucus: a thick liquid which is produced in parts of the body like the respiratory system

Muscles: tissues made up of cells which can contract and cause movement

N

Nervous system: the organ system consisting of brain, spinal cord, nerves and sense organs which controls an animals response to stimuli

Nitrates: minerals containing nitrogen which are essential for plant growth because they are used to make proteins

Non-identical (twins): twins formed when two eggs are fertilised at the same time, by different sperm, and form two different babies which are born together

Non-renewable (energy): energy source which cannot be used again and will run out eventually [eg fossil f uels]

Nucleus: the part of a cell that contains genes

Nutrients: substances obtained from food which are essential for healthy growth

O

Observations: the results of looking carefully at something and noticing properties or changes

Orbit: the path taken by one body in space around another (eg Earth around the Sun)

Ore: a rock that contains natural minerals from which useful substances can be extracted

Organs: group of tissues working together to do something useful to maintain an organisms life processes

Outlier: another name for an anomalous point

Oxygen: a non-metal element which exists as a gas in the atmosphere and is needed by most living things and for burning reactions

P

Particulates: tiny solid pieces of polluting substances in the air, for example soot

Payback time: time taken to recoup the cost of installing a type of home insulation (such as loft insulation)

Permanently extended: the irreversible extension of a spring when loaded beyond its elastic limit

Phosphates: minerals containing phosphorus which are essential for plant growth

Photocells: devices that transform light energy into electrical energy

Photosynthesis: the process by which green plants make their own food from carbon dioxide and water using solar energy

Physiologist: a scientist who studies living things

Phytoplankton: microscopic plants found in water

Pie chart: a way of presenting data when only one variable is a number

Placenta: organ which links the blood supply of a growing fetus with its mother's blood supply so that small molecules like nutrients, oxygen and waste products can pass from one to the other

Planet: any large body which orbits a star in a solar system

Polymer: a substance that has large molecules made up of atoms joined together in long chains

Population: a group of plants or animals living in the same place

Potassium: a mineral which is essential for plant growth

Precision: the number of decimal places given for a measurement

Predator: animal which catches, kills and eats other animals

Predict, predicting: saying what you think will happen

Pressure: a force applied by an object or fluid against a surface

Prey: animal which is hunted and eaten by other animals

Primary data: data collected directly by scientists for a particular investigation

Proportional: two related variables whose values increase at the same rate, eg when one is doubled the other doubles too

Psychologists: scientists who study what we do and why

R

Radiation: energy that travels as waves

Range: the numbers between the lowest and highest values a measurement can have, eg in the range 1-10

Reactants: substances which react together in a chemical reaction

Reaction time: in humans, the time the brain takes to process information and act

Reactivity series: a list of metals placed in order of their reactivity

Recycling: making new materials from materials that have already been used

Reflexes: inherited behaviours which cause animals to respond automatically to specific stimuli

Reforestation: planting trees to replace those that have been cut down

Relaxes: what happens when a muscle stops contracting and can be stretched

Reliable: an investigation is reliable if very similar data would be collected from the same investigation repeated under the same conditions

Remote sensing: collecting data at a distance , eg from a satellite

Renewable (energy): energy resources which are constantly being replaced and don't get used up (eg water or wind power are renewable energy sources)

Resistant: able to survive exposure to a substance that kills other organisms

Respiration: a chemical reaction in living things which releases energy from nutrients like glucose, usually by using oxygen

Respire: what organisms do to release energy from nutrients

Resultant force: the single force equivalent to two or more forces acting on an object

Retina: the layer of light sensitive cells at the back of the eye

Root hairs: the cells around the edge of a root that extend outwards to provide a large surface area to absorb water and minerals

S

Sacrificial protection: putting a more reactive metal in contact with a less reactive one so that the more reactive metal corrodes – the more reactive metal is sacrificed to protect the less reactive one

Sampling: choosing and making measurements on a small number of items from a bigger population, for example, to show what the whole population is like

Sankey diagrams: a diagram which shows all the energy transfers taking place in a process and the amount of energy in each transfer

Satellite: any body which orbits another (eg Moon around Earth, weather satellite around Earth)

Scaffold: a porous material that cells can grow around to produce a tissue with a specific shape like the windpipe

Secondary data: data collected by others which is used in an investigation

Sediment: very small pieces of solid which settles at the bottom of a liquid in a container or river

Sedimentary (rock): rock made from sediments joined together by pressure or chemicals

Selective breeding: producing offspring with desirable features by controlling which animals breed over many generations

Sense organs: organs which sense a stimulus like the eye, which detects light

Sensors: electronic devices that detect a changing signal

Sensory cells: cells that respond to stimuli such as light, touch, taste, smell and sounds

Sex cells: egg and sperm cells, which contain half as many genes as normal body cells

Social: animals that live in groups and communicate with each other

Solar cells: devices that transform light energy into electrical energy

Solar energy: energy from the Sun which can be used directly to make electricity or to heat water

Solar panels: devices that transform light energy into heat energy

Solar system: the Sun and the planets and other bodies in orbit around it

Soluble: a substance which can dissolve in a solvent

Solute: a substance which dissolves in a solvent to make a solution

Solution: a mixture of solvent and solute

Solvent: the liquid part of a solution

Specialised: a cell, tissue or organism that has features that perform specific functions eg muscle cells are specialised to produce movement because they can contract

Species: a group of organisms which can interbreed and produce fertile offspring

Speed: the distance travelled in a unit of time

Speed-time graph: shows how the speed of an object varies with time

Sports scientist: a scientist who researches and advises on the scientific aspects of sport and exercise

Springs: metal wound into spirals which can store elastic potential energy

Stamina: the ability carry on exercising for a long time

Stars: bodies in space which give out their own light – the Sun is a star

Steel: an alloy of iron with carbon and other elements

Stem cell: a cell which can divide and specialise to produce other types of cells – embryonic stem cells can produce any other type of cell but different adult stem cells produce a smaller number of different cells

Stimulant: a drug which speeds up your reactions and makes you more alert

Stimulation: making a sensory cell respond

Stimulus: something makes a sensory cell respond

Stomata: holes in leaves which allow gases to go in and out of the leaf (one hole is a stoma)

Streamlined: shaped to reduce resistance to motion from air or liquid

Sublime: to change directly from a solid to a gas

Sustainable: a process something that has a minimal effect on the environment

T

Temperature: a measure of how hot something is

Tendons: the connective tissue with connects muscles to bone

Tension: a stretching force

Terminal velocity: the highest velocity an object reaches when moving through a gas or a liquid; it happens when the drag force equals the forward force

Terraforming: changing an extraterrestrial environment, such as a planet, to support life

Theory: an idea that explains something

Tissues: a group of similar cells acting together

Transplant: the transfer of living tissue, or an organ, to someone else's body

Turbine: it turns when kinetic energy is transferred to it from steam, water or wind

U

Ultraviolet: electromagnetic radiation, especially from the Sun, important in tanning and some forms of skin cancer

Umbilical cord: the cord that connects the developing fetus to the placenta

Unbalanced (forces): when the opposing forces on an object are unequal

Unit (of alcohol): a measure of the amount of ethanol in an alcoholic drink

Uterus: the place where a baby develops and grows (womb)

V

Vacuole: large 'bag' inside the cell which is mostly full of water

Valves: a device that keeps blood circulating in the right direction

Variable: a quantity which can change eg time, temperature, length, mass. In investigations only one variable is allowed to change at a time to see what its effect is.

Variation: the differences between living things

Veins: wide, thin walled blood vessels which collect blood from the capillaries and carry it back to the heart

Velocity: speed in a particular direction

Vertebrate: an animal with a backbone

Visible light: electromagnetic radiation that is detected by the eye

Voltage: voltage is a measure of the strength of a cell or battery used to send a current around a circuit; voltage is measured in volts.

W

Wave power: a renewable energy resource

Weight: the result of the force of gravity on a mass

Wind farms: a collection of wind turbines

Wind turbines: devices that use the kinetic energy of the wind to produce electricity

X

Xylem vessels: tubes which carry water from a plant's roots to its leaves

Y

Yeast: a microbe (fungus) traditionally used to produce bread and alcohol which can be genetically modified to produce a variety of useful proteins eg for use as medicines

Yields: the amount of biomass produced by a plant

Index